Science in
Our Lives

SCIENCE

RITCHIE CALDER

IN OUR LIVES

MICHIGAN STATE COLLEGE PRESS
East Lansing

Published simultaneously in Canada by The Ryerson Press, Toronto

Manufactured in the United States of America
By The Haddon Craftsmen, Scranton, Pa.

CONTENTS

CONTENTS

PART

1

Merchants
of
Light

... *But thus you see we maintain a trade, not for gold, silver or jewels, nor for silks, nor for spices, nor any other commodity of matter; but only for God's first creature, which was light; to have light, I say, of the growth of all parts of the world.* ...

SIR FRANCIS BACON

Merchants of Light

1. THE LUNATICS

IN THE ENGLAND OF THE 1770's, The Lunatics used to meet once a month on the night of the full moon. And there was method in their madness because the moon was the lantern which had to light Erasmus Darwin home to Lichfield, "imprisoned in a post-chaise, joggled and jostled, and bump'd and bruised along the king's highroad," and Josiah Wedgwood on his forty miles' ride from Birmingham to The Potteries. Or, at least, it would help their horses to find their way, because Darwin and Wedgwood, abstemious men by the drinking standards of their day, were invariably intoxicated by the ferment of ideas which they had imbibed at the dining table of a coterie which helped to change the history of mankind.

Never more than ten ever sat down to dinner at The Lunar Society of Birmingham (inevitably called "The Lunatics"). No record was ever kept of its proceedings, lest the informality of its free-ranging discussions should be embarrassed; there were no transactions, no agenda, no resolutions and no programs of action. The one attempt of Matt Boulton to formalize it failed; it was like trying to pick up quicksilver with a fork.

They would discuss poetry and religion, arts and politics, music and science, with minds unbuttoned like their breeches-bands. Theirs was the spirit of universal inquiry which, somehow, we have lost today in a world in which the common ground of understanding has been fenced off into faculty estates and a barrier wall has been built between the humanities and science. We know more and we share less.

No such inhibitions or prohibitions restrained discussions of The Lunar Society which met in the homes of its sundry members. It was a free-for-all. James Watt, the inventor of the condensing steam engine, would argue music with William Herschel, the military bandsman who had become Private Astronomer to the King. Erasmus Darwin, physician, poet and philosopher, when he was not expounding creative evolution, would be telling Matt Boulton, Watt's partner, how to improve on some new mechanical invention. Josiah Wedgwood, the Prince of Potters, would exchange ideas about the separation of gases with Joseph Priestley, the discoverer of oxygen, who presently would be leading the debate on some theological subject. Samuel Galton would support Mr. Collins, the "rebel" guest from America, and Priestley would interrupt to read his latest letter from Benjamin Franklin.

It would be difficult to exaggerate the influence of The Lunar Society in terms of the men it brought around its table. They were a company of "Merchants of Light," as Francis Bacon called the twelve Fellows of The House of Salomon (in *New Atlantis*) whose commission was to seek everywhere for the facts of Nature and of human experience to illumine the minds of men.

The three founders of The Lunar Society were Matthew Boulton, William Small and Erasmus Darwin. Boulton was a toy maker ("toy" in those days meaning fine ornaments, like buckles for shoes and for knee breeches) and a minter of coinage, who had become the friend of Benjamin Franklin during the latter's second stay in England (1757-62).

Small had been introduced to Boulton by Franklin. This talented Scotsman had been Professor of Natural Philosophy at Williamsburg. One of his students had been Thomas Jefferson, who wrote in his autobiography that "Small probably fixed the destinies of my life." He may have done more than that when one considers the peculiar marks of scientific influence which are plain in the American Constitution. As Woodrow Wilson pointed out, the Constitution was based on a theory of political dynamics "which was a sort of unconscious copy of the Newtonian theory of the universe," a system of Government in which action and reaction are equal and opposite and all bodies are nicely poised by the balance of forces acting on them. Small left Williamsburg, with a letter of introduction from Franklin to Boulton, twenty-three years before the drafting of the Constitution, but he had helped to create the intellectual climate for it. With Boulton's help he became a physician in Birmingham.

* * *

In 1776, Boulton wrote to Franklin; he was in trouble. His factory at Soho, Birmingham, depended for its power on a brook, but in times of drought there was not enough water to drive the wheel. He had an idea of pumping the water from the tail of the millrace back to the milldam. This sounds crude, though ingenious, but it should be borne in mind that there was at that time no means of obtaining a rotary motion through steam power. The only thing which had been developed was a steam pump. Boulton wanted to adapt to his own design the Savory engine, which used steam itself as the piston, by direct pressure on the surface of the water. He sent the model to Franklin who, in this instance, had no practical suggestions to make, and Boulton had to go on experimenting. The answer, however, was to be found much nearer home—through his colleague of The Lunar Society, Dr. Small, who knew a Scots engineer named Watt.

Watt was "philosophical instrument maker" to the University of Glasgow, and two of his clients among the professors there were Joseph Black and John Anderson. It was Anderson who sent him a small model of the Newcomen engine to be repaired, "the cylinder being not more than one and a half inches in diameter and the boiler no more in size than a teakettle." Newcomen's engine was a piston pump. The boiler raised steam at low pressure. It had a rocking beam, pump rods on one end and a piston on the other. The rods drew up the piston, and when it was up, the cylinder filled with steam. Then the steam was cut off and cold water injected to condense the steam and produce a vacuum, so the pressure of the atmosphere forced down the piston. It thus tipped the rocking arm and raised the rods operating the pump. Watt realized how inefficient this was, but he was stuck for another answer.

He consulted Joseph Black, the professor of chemistry, the discoverer of carbon dioxide. Watt had himself found that a small quantity of water in the form of steam could heat a large quantity of water—six times its own weight—to its own temperature of 212 degrees Fahrenheit. Black then explained to Watt something which he had so far discussed only with his students, the theory of latent heat, for which he is famous. Its practical significance dawned on Watt as he walked over Glasgow Green. "I had not walked further than the Golf House," Watt wrote later, "when the whole thing was arranged in my mind; the waste of heat could be avoided by keeping the cylinder at steam-heat and condensing the steam in a separate boiler." He made a model (including his wife's thimble) and Black was so impressed that he loaned him £1,200 to continue his work. The result was the condensing steam engine and its decisive part in the Industrial Revolution.

But not yet. It needed the intervention of The Lunar Society: Small, concerned with his friend Boulton's problem, suggested that Watt should visit Birmingham. The result was a momentous partnership and the evolution of the Watt engine from a pump to a prime mover to drive the wheels of industry by reciprocating motion. Even here it is necessary to pause, for that would not have happened if, in the Birmingham group, there had not been Wilkinson, the cannon maker, who had produced fine lathes to turn accurately the bore of guns, and to whom the partners turned for the means of accurate boring of their cylinders.

* * *

In the weft and woof of ideas and personalities in this remarkable society, the pattern of the Industrial Revolution emerged. Watt gave it its power, but the developments of the cotton industry and of other textiles would not have been possible without the parallel development of the chemical industry and of, for example, bleaches for mass-produced fabrics. Keir gave the Industrial Revolution its synthetic alkalis and Roebuck gave it its sulphuric acid. Both were members of the Birmingham group. Watt introduced Berthollet, the French scientist, who communicated to the Society the process of bleaching by chlorine, and Watt's father-in-law, Mr. McGregor, whitened 1,500 yards of linen by it in 1798.

In that company was Dr. William Withering, the good physician, who had found a Shropshire granny brewing foxglove tea, and, being wiser than later generations of his kind who jeered at Old Wives' Tales, he sought its virtue and gave us *digitalis,* for the treatment of heart disease and dropsy. He was also a geologist and mineralogist who found and analyzed *witherite* (barium carbonate) which Wedgwood tried out in his pottery, later adding to it barium sulphate and producing his famous *jasper ware.* The barium sulphate was, incidentally, suggested by Keir, to Wedgwood, who found supplies by a personal geological search of Derbyshire. These Lunatics had a natural curiosity which turned into handsome profits!

And, of course, there was Erasmus Darwin, grandfather of Charles Darwin, but himself a "creative evolutionist" sixty years before his grandson upset the theologians by producing *The Origin of Species*. His *Zoonomia* gave plausible reasons "for believing the origin of species by transmutation possible" but, as Charles later pointed out, "he anticipated the views and erroneous grounds of opinion of Lamarck," and not the principle of natural selection. But Erasmus had other merits, not the least of them his generous humanitarianism. It is recorded that on his journeys as a physician he was twice held up by highwaymen and twice escaped with his life and his purse because they recognized him as the friend of the poor who would feed the sick rather than charge them a fee. He was a poet and an inventor and a philosopher whose unpopular opinions were always liable to get him into trouble.

*   *   *

But the one who encountered most trouble was Joseph Priestley, the friend of Benjamin Franklin. Priestley was a teacher at a dissenters' school in Warrington, Lancashire, when he became interested in Franklin's work on electricity and made the journey to London to see him. Franklin was then in the throes of the battle for the repeal of the Stamp Act, but he found time to see the young unknown and to inform and counsel him. His influence on Priestley was decisive and his inspiration largely responsible for the subsequent researches. It is noteworthy that it is to Priestley and not to Franklin himself that we owe the storybook account of how the kite-and-lightning experiment was carried out. Franklin never wrote the personal account of how he himself did it, referring to it in the *Gazette* only as "an experiment which succeeded in Philadelphia." But he told Priestley and approved his version of what happened:

> "Preparing, therefore, a large silk handkerchief and two cross-sticks of proper length on which to extend it, he took the opportunity of the first approaching thunder-storm to take a walk in the fields in which there was a shed convenient for

his purpose. But, dreading the ridicule which too commonly attends unsuccessful attempts in science, he communicated his intended experiment to nobody but his son"—then twenty-one, not a child as in the traditional illustrations of the scene —"who assisted him in raising the kite.

"The kite being raised, a considerable time elapsed before there was any appearance of its being electrified. One very promising cloud had passed over it without any effect: when, at length, just as he was beginning to despair of his contrivance, he observed some loose threads of the hempen string to stand erect, and to avoid one another, just as if they had been suspended on a common conductor. Struck with this promising appearance, he immediately presented his knuckle to the key [at the end of the twine] and (let the reader judge the exquisite pleasure he must have felt at that moment) the discovery was complete. He perceived a very evident electric spark." (Priestley, quoted by Carl Van Doren in *Benjamin Franklin*.)

The two were cronies, not only in their scientific pursuits but in the political activities in which Priestley engaged himself heavily, in support of the American colonists. It was Franklin who obtained Priestley's appointment as librarian to the Earl of Shelburne, the Secretary of State for the Colonies, in whose house he carried out his experiments which isolated oxygen. And it was through Franklin, that intellectual bee which pollinated so many minds and groups of minds, that Priestley came into touch with that rare company in Birmingham.

He moved there and became a member of The Lunar Society and minister of the Unitarian Church, but his financial situation was subtly adjusted by his fellow members, who, doing good by stealth, and with no affront to his pride, contrived that he should have the funds to carry on his researches. His work was at the very foundations of modern chemistry. This teacher of classics and dissenting preacher was one of the greatest experimenters of all times. But he had a philosophic blind spot—phlogiston. He accepted the theory of Stahl (1697) which assumed a hypothetical substance, "phlogiston," as the principle of combustion. This supposed that substances which burned were compounds of phlogiston and that combustion was caused by phlogiston leaving the substances. He was not converted by his fellow "Lunatic," Keir, who was an anti-phlogistonist. Nor did he notice, probably because of his preoccupation with the "fiery principle," the significance of "a mere random experiment made to entertain a few philosophical friends who have formed themselves into a private society, of which they have done me the honour to make me a member—to wit, The Lunar Society.

In this experiment he exploded "inflammable air" (hydrogen, discovered by Cavendish in 1776) and "dephlogisticated air" (oxygen, his own discovery in 1774) by an electric spark. A "dew" was formed on the glass container. In April, 1783, Priestley told Watt how he had found that the weight of the water thus formed was equal to the weight of the two gases. Watt immediately replied that this experiment showed the water to be a compound and not a single body, an "element." He subsequently wrote to Priestley:

> What are the products of your experiment? They are water, light and heat. Are we not, thence, authorized to conclude that water is a compound of the two gases, oxygen and hydrogen, deprived of a portion of their latent or elementary heat; that oxygen is water deprived of its hydrogen but still united to its latent heat and light; if light be only a modification of heat, or a simple circumstance of its modification, or a component part of hydrogen, oxygen gas will be water deprived of its hydrogen but combined with latent heat.

That was between cronies in a club and it was left to Cavendish to describe the composition of water to The Royal Society the following year (still in phlogiston terms) and for Lavoisier to show that Cavendish was wrong in thinking that the element water pre-existed in the gases and to state it in terms of oxygen and hydrogen. [There was scientific hijacking even in those days; Lavoisier made no acknowledgment of Cavendish nor of Priestley, nor of Watt, although the ignoring of the last is pardonable since the communication on the composition of water was a private letter to Priestley.]

Priestley persisted in sustaining phlogiston and in 1800 published, from America, his *Doctrine of Phlogiston Established and the Composition of Water Refuted*. Which was just too bad, because it has meant that Lavoisier is accepted as the father of modern chemistry. Not that Priestley would care; he liked research for its own sake and not for the rewards or the credits. And anyway, more portentous events had broken about his head and Lavoisier's.

* * *

The French Revolution had happened. The Lunar Society had been on the side of the Revolutionaries. James Watt's son, in Paris, had stopped a duel between Danton and Robespierre, and had been denounced by Thomas Burke in the House of Commons as a French agent. Priestley forgot his chemistry and became a vigorous supporter of the National Assembly. He, too, was denounced by Burke, while the French Revolutionists offered him French citizenship and nominated him a member of the National Convention, an honor he declined.

On July 14, 1791, James Keir, of The Lunar Society, held a dinner in the principal inn in Birmingham to celebrate the second anniversary of the Fall of the Bastille. It was open to sympathizers, who numbered eighty, but Priestley was at home with his wife and family. A mob collected outside the inn shouting "Church and King!" and smashed the windows. The object, however, was Priestley. They marched to The New Meeting House, of which he was Unitarian pastor, and set it on fire. Then they made for his house at Fairhill, a mile and a half away. But Priestley had been forewarned and escaped half an hour before their arrival. They smashed his home to smithereens, destroyed his apparatus and scattered his papers, ending with setting the house on fire. His manuscripts, the work of twenty years, were strewn around the countryside. The Lunatics were well aware of the dangers which they, as the unpopular "Philosophers," were facing. Boulton and Watt retreated to the Soho Manufactory and armed their workers for a state of siege. But the mob, having attacked houses with well-stocked cellars, were otherwise occupied.

Priestley shook the dust of Birmingham from his feet, took his family to London for safety and later emigrated to America, where he settled in Northumberland County, Pennsylvania. From there he dedicated his treatise *Experiments on the Generation of Air from Water* to his "valued friends, members of The Lunar Society of Birmingham."

Lavoisier was less fortunate. On May 8, 1794, the tumbrel

rattled into the Place de la Révolution. Lavoisier mounted the guillotine and the blade fell. "Only a moment to cut off his head," said his colleague, Lagrange, "and there will not be another like it for a hundred years."

The Lunar Society petered out after the opening of the nineteenth century. It had served its purpose.

2. THE FENCING-OFF OF SCIENCE

RICHARD LOVELL EDGEWORTH, a member of The Lunar Society, wrote:

A society of literary men and a literary society may be very different. In the one, men give the results of their serious researches and detail their deliberate thoughts. In the other, the first hints of discoveries, current observations, and mutual collision of ideas are of important utility. The knowledge of each member of such a society becomes, in time, disseminated among the whole body, and a certain *esprit de corps,* uncontaminated with jealousy, in some degree combines the talents of the members to forward the views of a simple person.

It is worth noticing that he refers to a "literary society" because "literary" in the parlance of the day did not mean merely the discussion of what was between the covers of a book, but "polite learning." It did not, as is also worth noticing, mean a "learned society," but referred to a group that was willing to "forward the views of a simple person."

* * *

This is more than just a play of words. The Lunar Society has been cited at some length in this part, which is concerned with science and the humanities, because it represented an approach to the problems of nature and of mankind which has been sacrificed in the intensive specialization of our times. That specialization has been forced upon us by the rapid advance of science and technology, which has created such a vast body of detailed knowledge that no one today can encompass it. To be proficient in any branch of science, an exponent has to concentrate upon the backlog and current developments in his subject almost to the ex-

clusion of every other interest. Even the members of The Lunar
Society, who indulged in such voluminous correspondence and
such omnivorous reading, would have been beaten by the forty
thousand scientific journals published in the world every year,
which have an output of over two million scientific contributions.

The result is that in place of the free-ranging discussions, with
wine and candlelight, at The Lunar Society, we have narrower
and narrower "briefings," in the ascetic glare of seminars and
colloquia, where in their private jargon, the gobbledygook of their
specialties, scientists discuss last week's meson, the latest amino-
acid synthesis or the hair on the whisker of a banana fly.

Learned societies, themselves splinter groups of natural philosophy, have subgroups within groups, subsects within sects. It is
not surprising, therefore, that the ordinary person begins to think
of science as a kind of vault with a lock, of which only a Ph.D.
knows the combination, and within it a series of safes labeled
"Physics," "Chemistry," "Biology," "Geology," "Astronomy,"
each again with its special combination lock, and inside these
safes, lockers—a vast number of lockers—marked "Nuclear
Physics," "Crystallography," "Solid State," "Colloid Chemistry,"
"Organic," "Inorganic," "Cytology," "Genetics," "Biophysics,"
"Biochemistry"; and what-have-you. And inside these more
caskets, also locked, with more and more precise labels, almost
ad infinitum.

Overspecialization is the curse of our age. Although it is un-
derstandable, even inevitable, it is still a curse because it gives
people the excuse for saying, "How can we understand?" and it
gives scientists the excuse for saying, "We have not time for other
subjects."

"An expert," it is said, "is one who knows more and more about
less and less." But there is another definition: "An expert is just
a perfectly ordinary guy a long, long way from home." He is a
babe lost in the forest which he cannot see for the trees.

That is a crude generalization, but it is substantially true in
the experience of those who have to live and work with experts,
particularly laboratory scientists. Of course, there are scientists
who, however specialized they may be in their laboratories, know
much of the facts of life and the graciousness of living, who appreciate cultural subjects and cultivate what is called "polite learning," and who can express themselves in the language of the

scientifically uninstructed. But they are exceptions. As a self-critical scientist once said: "Scientists are intellectual cripples. They only use part of their faculties and let the others languish."

* * *

The fault, however, is not all on the side of science. The preacher who complains that material advances in science are outstripping moral responsibilities piously says that he knows nothing of science. Statesmen, who boast their ignorance of science, nevertheless think themselves competent to legislate for the atomic bomb. The man in the saloon-bar, who ribs the "brainy guys," the "long hairs" and the "egg heads" of science, and blames them when a new device threatens his job or a new weapon threatens his home, does not bother to understand what science is about, and treats it as gadgeteering or escapes with it to the planets in a cartoon strip. He neither asks, "What makes a scientist tick?" nor, in alternating between fear and jeer, treats him as a life-sized individual, whose training has given him certain qualifications. People of this kind and the scientist are the victims of that kind of journalism which treats any scientific discovery as a miraculous revelation and every scientist as a genius.

Nevertheless, the divorce between science and the humanities is a serious problem and can create a desperate crisis in human affairs. Science is the pacemaker, the dynamic of our day and age. To take an obvious example: if medical science, equipped with penicillin and DDT and the armory of new drugs, can get rid of diseases, keep children alive to marry and multiply, and can extend the expectation of life, and if the science of food production does not keep pace, what then? (Later in this book this question will be faced.) But it also sets the pace (as the preachers complain) for moral philosophy, for politics and social change, and for education, the arts and literature.

But the exponents of these are reluctant, while recognizing it, to accept science as the pacemaker. They do not want to be dragged at its tail, so they imagine they can put the brakes on instead of climbing on board and helping to steer it. For instance, when UNESCO was conceived at the end of the war, it was as "UNECO" —the United Nations Educational and Cultural Organization. There was no "S" for "Scientific." The "S" was inserted mainly through the efforts of the U. S. Delegation and the influence of

Archibald MacLeish (the poet, mind you) at the Preparatory Commission in London. But the resistance was significant. The pedagogues regarded science as something which was to be found in educational textbooks or taught in laboratories; the esthetes thought of science as something which, with grace and patina of time, might qualify as culture. They did not, or would not, accept it as the pacemaker for both education and culture. They were prevailed upon eventually, but one suspects that it was because they thought the "S" ought to be safely handcuffed between the E and the C!

Science is not something which is just taught in school to those who choose to study it. It is something which alters the nature of education itself because it is the factor which is changing the world and the conditions of society for which students are being trained. Because science is so often regarded as vocational training for those who are going on to scientific degrees or technical jobs, education tends to become warped. All students ought to be taught what science means, what its thought processes are and what its social effects are likely to be. This does not mean learning all the technicalities of science; it means that the student "takes science in his stride." The example set by Dr. James Conant when he was president of Harvard in giving lectures on science to the liberal arts courses could well be extended more widely in other universities. Some, in the United States, have instituted such courses.

3. SCIENCE AND CULTURE

THE DIVORCE BETWEEN SCIENCE AND CULTURE IS ABSURD. To hear some people talk, you would think that science had destroyed art or had corrupted it into modern forms which should be regarded as distasteful. And they lament that the Golden Age will come again only when science is, somehow, discarded. That is utter nonsense. "What is this Golden Age of Art untarnished by the breath of rude mechanics?" demands Dr. J. Bronowski who in *The Common Sense of Science* (Harvard University Press) brilliantly takes up the challenge.

What? and when? Let us go back six thousand years to the Egyptians. We find that they had already divided the length of the year into three hundred and sixty-five days by counting the days which intervened between two successive occasions when the Dog

Star, Sirius, was just visible at its rising immediately before sunrise. Between then and the building of the Great Pyramid, about 2800 B.C., the Egyptians developed the science of measurement, distance and direction. All the pyramids are extraordinary examples of practical mathematics in terms of their shape and construction. But consider the Great Pyramid: it was so designed that the rays of Sirius struck it at right angles. One ventilating shaft was so placed that it admitted the light of the star when it crossed the meridian to penetrate to the Royal Chamber in the heart of the Pyramid and "miraculously" lit up the face of the dead Pharaoh. Is the Great Pyramid an object of art (it certainly is of culture) or of science?

"Pythagoras lived before Aeschylus created Greek drama. Socrates taught when that drama was at its greatest. Is Socrates to be claimed for art or for science?" asks Bronowski.

We speak of the Golden Age of Rome. What of Lucretius, the greatest of all didactic poets who died in the year Julius Caesar invaded Britain? He was not only a great poet but a pioneer in poetry, for he found the hexameter rough and crude, and polished it into a fine instrument for Virgil to use. A poet, yes, but a scientist too. In poetic language unsurpassed not only in Latin but in any human speech, he wrote *De Rerum Natura,* a scientific thesis, attacking superstition; describing natural phenomena; stating that soul and mind were integral parts of the human body and no more capable of having a separate existence than a hand or foot can; discoursing upon the nature of disease; and discussing the origin of the world, of the rise and progress of Man and the beginnings of civilization and society. He grasped that time is a relative thing. His views on heredity were at least consistent with those of Mendel. And he gave a credible account of natural selection. His atomic theory envisaged the primal universe as containing an infinite number of infinitesimal particles falling through infinite space. They swerve, meet and clash, building up small units (what we would now call molecules) aggregating into larger masses and finally into worlds. Living creatures were a chance conglomeration of atoms with Life an interaction between them. Newton was to return to this classical theory seventeen hundred years later. John Dalton, by experimental observation in the nineteenth century, elaborated, from Lucretius, his atomic weights and his fundamental laws. Is Lucretius, therefore, a poet or a scientist?

We know Omar Khayyám (eleventh century) as the poet of the

Rubáiyát, but when in modern Persia I spoke at Teheran University of "Your great poet, Omar Khayyam," my audience looked puzzled: they knew him as their greatest astronomer and mathematician.

Leonardo da Vinci (1452-1519), creator of *The Last Supper* and *The Mona Lisa,* was a supreme scientist as well as a supreme artist. He was an anatomist, an engineer, an architect. He was a paleontologist who challenged the story of The Flood; a cosmologist who just mentioned casually, "The Sun does not move," at a time when he could have been burned at the stake for such a heresy; the inventor of the *camera obscura,* of the hygrometer for measuring the moisture in the atmosphere, of the submarine and of breach-loading guns. Did his science destroy his art?

Sir Francis Bacon is claimed by belles-lettres for his essays (and by some zealots, as the author of the works of Shakespeare), but he is also claimed by science as the father of modern experimental science. He belonged to the Golden Age of Queen Elizabeth, when poetry and literature marched triumphantly with the science of the great navigators.

Another Golden Age (so called) was the Restoration. But one of the earliest acts of Charles II on his return was to become the patron of The Royal Society, "an enterprise for the Benefit of Human Life by the Advancement of Real Knowledge." Its members included Sir Christopher Wren, architect of St. Paul's; Robert Boyle, of Boyle's Law; Flamsteed, the astronomer; John Evelyn, the diarist; Hooke, one of the greatest experimenters of all time; Petty, the father of economics or, as he called it, "Political Arithmetick;" John Winthrop, governor of Connecticut; Bishop Sprat; Samuel Pepys and John Dryden. There was no contention between the arts and science here; they belonged together.

And did Milton's attempt to introduce science into his teaching at the Aldersgate school tarnish the gold of *Paradise Lost?*

But, say some critical esthetes, science by explaining the wonders of Nature robs it of its wonderment. Newton took the rainbow to pieces when he explained the nature of light and used the prism to reproduce the rainbow, breaking light down into its component colors. That did not take away the vision of the artist or the inspiration of the poet. Indeed, a scientist wanting to prove this statistically has worked out that Alexander Pope, Newton's contemporary, uses four times as many color words as Shakespeare and uses them ten times as often. The beautiful experiments with color which Newton carried out had a vivid effect on the poets and painters of the eighteenth century.

* * *

Again it is said that the Industrial Revolution, powered by science, smothered the arts with the commonplace as it smothered cities with soot. But the critics cannot have it both ways: the Romantic Revival coincided with the advent of the steam engine.

Since the arts are influenced by the circumstances and emotional and intellectual climate of their times, science does affect them, either actively or reactively (e.g., Blake accepting the challenge of the Industrial Revolution realistically in his *Jerusalem* or Walter Scott escaping romantically into *Ivanhoe*). As Dr. Bronowski suggests (in *The Common Sense of Science*), the mechanistic philosophy of cause and effect, with its sense of scientific determinacy or predestination, gave writers an air of pessimism which overhung the novel from Thomas Hardy to Virginia Woolf.

As he also points out: "The invention of printing does not seem to bear very directly on the content of poetry. But when a poem can be read and read again, it is natural that the interest shifts from the rhythm to the meaning and the allusion. So the invention of photography has made the painter and the patron lose interest in the likeness and transfer it to the more formal pattern."

If, however, we extend that argument, science has probably given more to the arts than some esthetes think it has taken from them. It has opened up whole new realms of Nature in the appreciation and expression of which the artists and poets are still only experimenting. The Institute of Contemporary Arts in London (which includes many scientists) has held exhibitions and produced a book, *Aspects of Form,* as a general survey of visual form from physics through biology and psychology to art. These have shown the pattern revealed in the X-ray pictures of crystals, electron-microscope pictures of cellulose structure and the electro-encephalograph versions of the activity of the human brain. At the Festival of Britain, carpets and textiles were produced with patterns which even the esthetic Tuscans could not forbear to cheer—until they were told that they were models of the atom and the atomic structure of a molecule of penicillin!

But the challenge of science to the arts is more apparent in the media it has created—the film, radio and television—and in new materials it can make available. As a film producer said, "Three-dimensional films are upon us before we have mastered the art forms of the silent film, let alone the talkies." If, as Bronowski has pointed out, printing altered the interest from rhythm to meaning and allusion, what are going to be the effects of radio on the form of poetry, of drama and of the spoken word—"mouth music"—generally? And of television?

4. THE CHALLENGE TO THE ARTS

THERE IS, HOWEVER, an even bigger challenge to the arts—that is, the audience which science has made available. If the result is not to be vulgarization but a raising of popular appreciation, the script writers, the poets, the dramatists, the musicians and, indeed, the artists have to re-examine their own values and forms. The real Golden Age of the arts will come about when the enduring values of culture are not just the privilege of a cultured *élite* but are shared with the many.

The divorce of science and the arts has produced another fallacy—that a scientific training somehow unfits its "victims" for appreciation or exposition of the arts. A poll of scientists would reveal that a large proportion of them are (a) good chess players and (b) good musicians. The first is to be expected, since the discipline of science is a good preparation for chess. The second may surprise some people, yet Einstein, the Kreisler of Relativity, and Sir James Jeans, the organist of the Cosmos, are famous examples of the many. And there are poets and artists and writers in the ranks of the scientists. And there are Philistines, too.

Leaving exposition aside, let us consider appreciation which is, if you like, a passive cultural attainment. Suppose three people are listening to a concerto on the radio. One is a musician, that is, he knows the theory and practice of music; the second is a scientist who knows about wave propagation and radio frequencies; and the third is a technician who knows how to make a radio set. Their enjoyment is spoiled by a false note. The musician wants to strangle the first violinist. The scientist thinks of sunspots. The technician thinks that something is wrong with the fidelity of his receiver. It is immaterial which is the right explanation. What is material is that they have the proper appreciation and know that something is spoiling the music.

Of course, scientists ought to be introduced to the liberal arts just as everyone ought to be introduced to science, but, apart from the preoccupations of specialization, there is no reason why science and "polite learning" should be mutually exclusive.

5. SCIENCE AND RELIGION

THERE IS ALSO THE AGE-OLD CONFLICT between science and religion. So far as religion relies on magic and superstition, the conflict is complete, for science exists to destroy superstition and to find rational explanations for natural phenomena which the superstitious regard as supernatural. As Sir Francis Bacon put it in describing his House of Salomon in *New Atlantis:*

> We have also houses of deceit of the senses, where we represent all manner of feats of juggling, false apparitions, impostures and illusions and their fallacies. And surely you will easily believe that we, that have so many things truly natural which induce admiration, could in the world of particulars deceive the senses if we would disguise those things and labor to make them more miraculous. But we do hate all impostures and lies insomuch as we have severely forbidden it to all our fellows, under pain of ignominy and fines, that they do not show any natural work, or thing, adorned or swelling, but only pure as it is, and without all affectation of strangeness.

But to suggest that science and religion cancel each other out is absurd. Science has been defined as "Proof without Certainty" and Faith as "Certainty without Proof." (Theologians may argue that Revelation is proof; but a scientist, even a bigoted churchman like Michael Faraday, has never measured Revelation.) The scientist who says, "I am an atheist" is being dogmatic and unscientific; he can, as a scientist, only say, "I am an agnostic" meaning, "I do not *know* that God exists." Nor can he deny belief. Every time he frames a hypothesis on the observable facts and says, "Therefore, I believe such and such to be true," it is a convenient supposition until his subsequent experiments prove or disprove it, and then his *belief* becomes a *fact*—but never a *certainty,* because subsequent knowledge may modify his conclusion. (Newton's Laws looked like a statement of certainty, but they have been modified by Einstein.)

"Religion and science," said the late Sir Richard Gregory, the great editor of "Nature," in his book *Religion in Science and Civilization,* "are the two chief factors which have influenced human development throughout all stages of civilization: religion is the reaction to an inner impulse as to what is conceived to be sacred and arouses awe or reverence; and science is the accumulation of knowledge of the properties of natural objects—animate and inanimate—in relation to Man's needs and his understanding of them through the use of his intelligence. One represents the emotional side of Man's nature as expressed in religious ritual art and literature; the other—also a product of an inner urge—is the construction of a mental picture of what is known, at any stage of an inquiry, about the nature of all things, visible and invisible."

"It is," he added, "in the light of service to high ideals that science, without which we cannot live, and religion, without which most people see no meaning in life, can find a common field for action."

Individual scientists belong to all manner of religious beliefs and sects, or to none. Or some may call themselves "scientific humanists," believing that essential goodness lies in the betterment of mankind, through the exercise of human reason and the benefits of science. Or some may follow Marxist materialism and discard religion in its spiritual and ritualistic sense as the drug of reason, and the deception of the masses. Each can believe what he likes, because, as Sir Richard Gregory put it, "science does not set out to establish or depose any particular articles of belief or substance of faith, but only to examine critically whatever comes before it in the natural world and to testify faithfully to what is seen and what it seems to reveal."

Descartes, a scientist who distinguished between soul and body, said that he studied science "in order to know how to distinguish truth from falsehood, so as to be clear about my actions and to walk surefootedly in this life."

Whatever a scientist thinks or believes, he must approach every problem as a skeptic; he must neither invent nor discard evidence to suit his hypothesis, whether it be a scientific or religious assumption, and he must "testify faithfully." Beyond that, he is like the rest of us.

* * *

The historic collisions were not between science and faith but between science and obscurantism, which opposes the progress of knowledge and denies anything which conflicts with an accepted system. The Church which made Galileo recant and burned Bruno at the stake because he persisted that the earth was not the center of the universe, that it moved round the sun, that the universe was infinite and that it was permeated throughout by a common soul, also burned heretics and witches. Any natural law or supernatural belief which conflicted with doctrine had to be rejected. The professor of philosophy at Padua University who refused to look through Galileo's telescope at the mountains of the moon was not constrained by the Christian religion, but by the philosophy of the pagan Aristotle. He just did not want to see anything which conflicted with his beliefs.

The same was true in the ferocious battles of the nineteenth century between the theologians and the Darwinians over *The Origin of Man.* Just as the earth before Copernicus had been the center of the universe, so Man was the special object of creation, and, according to Bishop Usher (1580-1656), whose chronology was included in the *Authorized Version of the Bible,* the world was created in 4004 B.C. The evidence of the rocks proved this time scale to be impossible (but the obscurantists suggested that God on that morning of Creation deliberately sandwiched in the fossil skeletons), and now evolution was claiming that Man had common ancestry with the apes! Bishop Wilberforce and Thomas Huxley fought it out in the public arena, and left people with the impression that science and religion were irreconcilable when it was a question of how best to assimilate the new knowledge.

6. SCIENCE AND EDUCATION

BUT NEW KNOWLEDGE, emerging every day from our laboratories, affects more than our religious or philosophic concepts; it affects the whole structure of our material existence and our social institutions. It has to be assimilated at many levels, not least by the ordinary people, whose lives and livelihoods are involved.

Three hundred years ago, Jan Comenius, the great Czech, had an idea of how it might be done. His ideas of education command the respect of educationists today, but there was one aspect of his contribution which particularly affects science; that was his *Pansophicon*. There is no doubt that it was inspired by Sir Francis Bacon's House of Salomon, but Comenius spelled it out. His idea was to create a college at which the wise men of the world would come together, for a year at a time, and bring with them, and assess and explore, all the natural knowledge, collected from all over the world, and propound it and make it widely known for the adoption by men for their benefit. It was an idea which appealed to the burgeoning minds in Britain and he was invited to London. His enterprise was so well received that the Seminary of St. James's, Chelsea, was earmarked for the college. The ways and means were to be discussed in Parliament in the fateful session in which the Civil War broke out. Charles I lost his head; Comenius lost his college and the building which had been assigned was given by Charles II, at the instigation of Nell Gwyn, to house military veterans. Today the Royal Chelsea Hospital for Pensioners is where Pansophicon might have been. The idea did not become entirely lost; it influenced the virtuosi who met as The Invisible College, first in London and then at Oxford, and who conceived The Royal Society of London, the prototype of the National Academies. In its way, The Lunar Society was an offspring of Pansophicon. And today the Princeton Institute of Advanced Studies reflects Comenius' intention.

But it is not only on the high intellectual level of synthesis and assimilation, as at Princeton, that Comenius needs his present-day expression. We need a heart pump to spread the corpuscles of science through the body politic.

We have to restore something of the inquiring spirit and common understanding which was shared by the members to The Lunar Society and personified in that one-man Pansophicon, Benjamin Franklin.

PART

2

Scientific

Method

. . . Man can learn nothing unless he proceeds
from the known to the unknown. . . .

CLAUDE BERNARD

Scientific Method

1. SCIENCE GOES TO TRIAL

IN THE SILENCE ROOM OF THE LONDON CLUB to which bishops escape from Convocation and scientists from The Royal Society, one finds the common ground of science and religion. In its plushlike hush, you will find both men of the crucifix and the crucible asleep in their chairs or reading detective stories.

Then, as though the plush had been rubbed with amber, there is a crackle of mild static which makes the attendant's hair stand on end; it is the Bishop of Barchester flagrantly breaking the rule and whispering to his neighbor, the Oxbridge professor of natural philosophy.

"I see you and I are reading the same thriller," he whispers. "I suggest that you concentrate on the means and methods and that I concentrate on the human motivations, and we'll see who discovers the scoundrel first."

*　　*　　*

There is a very good reason why scientists are addicted to detective fiction: a well-written "whodunit" is a leisure-hour scientific thesis. For crime-detection depends essentially on the scientific method—observation, hypothesis, experiment, theory and proof. *Observation* is the collection of the available facts; *hypothesis* is the tentative assumption made from these facts; experiment is the testing of the facts in the light of the assumption; *theory* is the hypothesis when it has become respectable enough to justify holding the suspect; and the *proof* is what the prosecutor needs to support the theory before a jury.

Let us take an example from a real-life murder in which I, as a crime-reporter, was involved:

A man, George Welham, was found shot in a lonely wooden hut, in the fields of a dog-breeding establishment. The body was on the floor lying on its back with the gun underneath, and a twig near-by with the victim's fingerprints on it. Pieces of bark from the twig were found on the trigger. The back of Welham's skull had been shattered, and blood and buckshot had spattered onto a plywood board covering the wall, alongside a desk and in the direction in which the body was lying.

The first hypothesis, made by the local police, was suicide, based partly on the observations of the position of the body and the twig which, they pointed out, "had been used to fire the trigger"; but partly on intuition. They recalled that Welham's partner had been found dead in the recesses of a wood, shot, also with a buckshot gun. The partner had been missing for some days, but Welham had found him, led, so he said, by the dead man's dog. The verdict had been accidental death, but the local police had suspected that Welham had murdered him. A few months before his own death Welham had had a car accident and become moody. The local police said it was his conscience, and that it had driven him to suicide. All very interesting, with the sort of human motivation which might have satisfied the Bishop of Barchester. But not the professor of natural philosophy.

Anyway, the first hypothesis was demolished by the police surgeon who proved that, in spite of the bark on the trigger, only an acrobat could have shot himself, and produced the particular head wounds, in the circumstances in which the body was found. So Scotland Yard was called in to test the new hypothesis—murder.

I was with the inspector when he started making his new observations. He concentrated on the plywood board. First, on the bloodstains. The spots had hit the board at an angle which could not correspond to the body having been on the floor. Then, on the buckshot holes. Patiently he whittled matchsticks and inserted them into each of the holes. To each he tied a thread and brought all the threads to a focus, which would have been the muzzle of the gun. The direction of the threads lay across the desk to a point beyond the desk and four feet inside the door. Further reconstruction showed that the gun was pointing downwards, from a shoulder five feet two inches from the ground, aiming at the back of the man who was sitting at the desk but crouching over it. The "crouching" was important, because the wound in the victim's head and the angle of the buckshot in the plyboard were consistent with his having ducked without turning his head.

The inspector then erected his theory. The victim had been sitting at his desk writing. Someone had entered the hut through the door and had pointed the gun at him. The victim had instinctively sensed the gun directed at him and had ducked sideways over the corner of the desk to avoid the shot. This explained why there was no blood on the desk itself and was sustained by marks on the desk.

Here then was support for the theory of murder. It would have given the professor of natural philosophy his "means and method," by exact measurements.

I should like to be able to say that we convicted the murderer. Unfortunately, no. It was not an "unsolved murder"; it was an "unproven murder."

The inspector proceeded from a second hypothesis—that the murderer was someone the victim knew and was accustomed to have around because he knew someone was there behind him but went on working. We tested this. For example, the door creaked and could not be opened stealthily (it was cold weather, so it must have been closed), and the floorboards groaned under the step of any man. So whoever was there was not a furtive intruder but someone whom the victim knew was in the room and knew well enough to ignore. And there were other factors which pointed to one person—I, like the inspector, had no doubts that his theory as to the murderer was right, but the theory could not be proved "beyond the shadow of a doubt." And the missing factor was the Bishop of Barchester's "human motivation."

2. THE DETECTIVE AND THE ATOM

RESEARCH AND CRIME-DETECTION have a lot in common, but the research worker is like that Scotland Yard detective and not like the fellow who writes the detective stories. The writer thinks out his plot (his theory) and then produces the facts to conform. He is rather like the classical theorists who dominated natural philosophy for two thousand years until Sir Francis Bacon defined the principles of modern research at the beginning of the seventeenth century. The classical theorists were *deductive;* they proceeded from the general to the particular; they erected a model theory as to how things ought to behave, and if they did not behave accordingly, they were against reason, since reason (on their reasoning) could not be wrong. Modern science is *inductive,* moving from the particular to the general, from the buckshot holes to the theory of the crime. The experimental scientist finds the evidence, fits the clues together and proves his answer before the jury of his critical colleagues.

The late Lord Rutherford, pioneer of atomic research, was very like my friend, the Scotland Yard inspector, and what is more, he had little patience with those clever logicians who could evolve beautiful theories and perfect equations and whose reasoning and arguments were so perfect (like the gifted criminologist of detective fiction) as to be flawless. He made an exception in the case of Niels Bohr, the Danish theoretical physicist. "But, after all," Rutherford would say, "Bohr's different. He's a football player!"

But Rutherford, like the real-life detective, would seize upon clues, examine their significance, deduce the possible explanation and then patiently and simply reconstruct what might have happened. He would then produce a theory, but it would be based upon experimental factors and would be tested by experimental follow-up. His great capacity was in spotting clues which others might miss, realizing, often intuitively, what was behind them and then, metaphorically, whittling matchsticks and plugging them in the buckshot holes.

*   *   *

One of Rutherford's greatest discoveries is an excellent example of this: among his research students at Manchester was a German, Geiger, whose name is perpetuated in the Geiger counter, one of the most important tools in atomic work today. To him he suggested following up something which had, some years before, struck him as curious—that a beam of alpha particles from a radioactive source was scattered in passing through a thin film of aluminum. (The effect on the invisible rays was like that on a beam from a Kleig light when, in order not to be unkind to the fading beauties of a film star, it is masked with butter muslin.) Geiger and a colleague, Marsden, set to work. They used thin films of gold which is almost "transparent" to alpha rays, but they found that a considerable proportion of the rays was deflected at an angle of ninety degrees. Rutherford was flabbergasted. "It's as though a fifteen-inch shell were being bounced off a sheet of tissue paper," he said.

Alpha rays were not easily deflected in this way. In experiments an enormous electric field was needed to turn them through an angle of ninety degrees. How could such an electric field exist in such a thin piece of foil? It was baffling, and for days Rutherford went around the laboratory humming dolefully "Fight the good Fight"—a sure sign that he was unhappily perplexed. Then one day he bounced into the laboratory humming "Onward Christian Soldiers"—a sure sign that he was in great good humor. "Geiger," he cried, "I now know why your particles are kicked around and what an atom looks like!"

This was how he had reasoned on the facts available: the particles fired by an exploding radioactive atom traveled in straight lines (like the buckshot from the gun). These alpha particles passed through matter, not by pushing the atoms aside nor by swerving to avoid them, but by *passing through* the atoms themselves. Therefore, atoms could not be solid as the prevailing idea then was. "So," argued Rutherford, "they must be like solar systems—not solid spheres." The invading alpha particles would thus be able to traverse the empty space between the central sun and the planets of this system. This system would be held together by the fact that the "planets" would be negatively charged electrons and the "sun" a positively charged nucleus. This nucleus would contain most of the mass of the atom, but would be a relatively small part of its volume as contained by the circumference of the electrons in their orbits. The strong central field which would thus be created would account for the bending of the alpha rays, since the positively charged alpha particles (helium nuclei, in fact) would be violently repelled if they came near the positively charged nucleus.

He put forward his hypothesis in 1911, but kept Geiger and Marsden experimentally checking and rechecking for another two years until their repeated results promoted his hypothesis to a theory, to be expressed in the Rutherford-Bohr Model (subsequently modified but the first conceptual "picture"). Bohr, who had come to Rutherford as a twenty-seven-year-old mathematician (redeemed by a pair of football boots), worked out the orbits of the electrons on a basis which has stood the test of time and the test of millions of experiments. In its simplest form—the hydrogen atom—a single electron rotates around a single proton. The outer boundary which it patrols gives the atom a diameter which is about one hundred millionth of an inch. The nucleus—

the single proton—has a diameter of only a tenth of a million-millionth of an inch. In the heavier atoms the orbits get more complicated until the model of the uranium atom, with its ninety-two electrons looks like a ball of knitting wool.

So *inductive* science—experiment to theory, with theory confirmed by experiment—has taken us a long way from the solid atoms of Democritus, *deductively* conceived in the fifth century B.C.

3. THE JARGON OF SCIENCE

THE COMPLEXITIES OF, SAY, NUCLEAR PHYSICS, which bewilder ordinary folks, are caused by the vast accumulation of data and the enormous glossary of nuclear terms, but the facts have been arrived at step by step in much the same way as Rutherford arrived at the first picture of the atom. And as for nomenclature, it is not so very terrifying if one remembers, for example, that he called it "Alpha particle" from the Greek letter "A" just because he found that in the radiation from uranium (first recognized by Becquerel) there were two different kinds. So he called them "A" and "B". The "B" or "Beta" rays are electrons, but they are fired off by uranium with much greater force than they are by the heated filament of a radio tube. The relative force might be grasped in the comparison between soot rising from a fire which would smudge your face and the grains of cordite from a cartridge which would pit your face with indelible tattoo marks.

Science has been defined as a body of knowledge. But that means about as much as saying that you can find all the works of Shakespeare in the dictionary, because all the words are there. One of the things which blocked scientific progress for nearly two thousand years was the idea that the Greeks had had the last word for it, that the knowledge existed. And such knowledge, untested by experiment, could be adapted or interpreted to suit the beliefs of the times, or to conform to doctrine. A "body of knowledge" unchallenged and unreplenished goes sick and may become itself superstition—like astrology, which started off as that exercise of observation and reason which we call astronomy, the charting of the stars in their courses. No, science is not just knowledge; it is knowledge working for its living, correcting itself, and adding to itself.

4. HOW SCIENCE BEGAN

SCIENCE, THEREFORE, IS A PROCESS. But how did it begin? It began when Man began to observe and make a note of his observations. In the Stone Age, Man lived on the flesh of the animals he could slay. Primitive men were creatures of superstition and probably, like the practitioners of voodoo who make wax models of their enemies and stick pins in them, they made drawings of these animals in the act of being slain in the hope that the wish would be fulfilled. So we have representations of bison in the cavern of Maux, in the south of France, which are faithful anatomical studies, with the arrow penetrating exactly where the heart would be. This, apart from any superstition, showed a useful "know-how" in killing animals.

Then men noticed that the grains in certain grasses were specially good to eat; that from seed they could grow new grasses, that if they chose a suitable bit of ground they could grow lots of such grasses: and that if they scraped the ground, the plants would root better. So they became tillers, applying the science of their observations.

But agriculture depends on the seasons (another observation of the early scientists), and they needed a calendar to help them to sow and reap. They noticed that certain stars had a fixed relationship to the sun, which corresponded with their seasons of growth. And their preoccupation with the stars for this simple purpose of living led them to more—shall we say—academic observations. Five thousand years ago, before, or about the time when Bishop Usher would have us believe Abraham left Ur of the Chaldees, astronomers there could predict an eclipse as recurring at an interval of eighteen years and eleven days. Complete records extending over 360 years have been found at Ur and in them the evidence that a Chaldean, without help of the accurate instruments now at our disposal, had worked out the length of the year as 365 days 6 hours 15 minutes and 41 seconds, only 26 minutes and 26 seconds too long.

Such calendar-making was characteristic of most cultures—the Mayan and Aztec calendars are half a world apart from those of the Middle East, but are just as remarkable in their observations.

When the Nile flooded, it swept away the natural landmarks

which might have divided one tiller's ground from another. So some method had to be devised by which the land could be marked out every year. That was the origin of practical geometry. The Egyptians invented a set square to give a right angle by knotting a rope in lengths of three units, four units and five units (the units being based on the length from the tip of the middle finger to the elbow), and pegging it on the ground at the knots. From such practical devices, the Greeks later produced their logical systems of geometry (although Chinese prints of 1000 B.C. show the Orientals anticipated the famous theorem of Pythagoras—that the square on the longest side of a right-angled triangle is the sum of the squares of the other two; and excavations at Tel-el-Harmel near Baghdad showed that much of Euclid was anticipated by two thousand years.)

When men began to congregate in communities and to trade, they needed numbers. The handiest way was, like a child at school, counting the fingers. So we have from earliest times had ten-finger, decimal counting. Or men notched sticks, like the bad man of the cowboy films notching his gun to keep tally of his victims. Then they found it was easier to count pebbles. And the next stage was to have the pebbles in a convenient form, so they strung them together as the abacus, or counting frame. The Mexicans and Peruvians were using the abacus before the Spaniards arrived in the New World. The Chinese and Egyptians possessed the abacus a thousand years before the Christian Era. The Romans borrowed it from the Etruscans.

Having tallied up the score, it was necessary to make a note of it. So numerals were introduced. The numerals we use today are derived from the Hindus and probably are the initials of the Hindu words conveying "two," "three," "four," and so on. And zero was probably the unhatched egg.

With the now recognizable stars to guide them, people could guide themselves overland (and most of this was happening in lands where skies were rarely overcast), but underground it was different. Underground? Yes, five thousand years ago in Persia men started to dig *qanats,* or horizontal wells, along the courses of the underground springs, with vertical shafts at intervals, all the way back to their sources in the hills. For their mining, to give them direction, they used a primitive lodestone compass. It may have originated there in Persia; it may have come from China; in any event, it reached the Mediterranean to become the magnetic compass to aid the great navigations and, eventually, through Faraday's use of the magnet, to produce electrical generation.

So knowledge progressed, from finding answers to practical problems, making observations, compiling observations (as in the calendar priesthoods) and building up systems. But these were slave civilizations in which the slaves did the work and the masters did the thinking. And that was particularly true in Ancient Greece where the classical thought-processes reached their zenith. Reasoning was regarded as the highest attribute of men. Some like Aristotle (384-322 B.C.) actually made thorough observations and experiments, as in his naturalistic studies and his *Parts of Animals,* which evoke the admiration of experimental scientists today. In his biological work, Aristotle was therefore an *inductive* scientist proceeding from the particular to the general, but in his theories of the universe and man's relations to it, he was, like Plato, his master, a *deductive* scientist. He produced his theory of the universe of which the world was the center surrounded by a sphere of atmosphere; then by the upper elements, earthly exhalation, water, air and fire; then the planets; then a sphere of fixed stars; and then the sphere of divine harmony, which caused the circular revolution of the whole celestial system. Because Bruno, nearly two thousand years later, dared to challenge this concept, he was burned at the stake.

Plato (427-347 B.C.) was largely responsible for the role of mathematics in modern education, not merely as an instrument for practical ends, but as the training of logical thought. He was the abstract theoretician. Because any irregularities in the planetary motion were inconsistent with his ideally perfect universe, all heavenly bodies must move in circles and they must be perfect spheres. This was quite useful as a guiding principle, but it was not true. Kepler (1571-1630), a devout Platonist, had to rebut his master and show that the planets move around the sun, not in circles, but in ellipses. Later, Galileo's telescope showed that the moon was rough and mountainous like the earth, and the whole Platonic idea of "perfection" of heavenly bodies was discredited.

Just how absurd this kind of reasoning can be is illustrated by the example of Platonic "perfection" as argued in the Middle Ages:

The male sex was more perfect than the female. The circle was the perfect shape. Hens being imperfect females laid imperfect eggs—pointed ovals. But some eggs were less imperfect than others, more nearly the ideal round, and it was from these that cockerels would hatch.

Grown men would solemnly argue this when the simplest observation of eggs as they hatched would have shown it was nonsense.

5. THE TWILIGHT OF SCIENCE

THIS KIND OF ATTITUDE PREVAILED throughout the Dark and Middle Ages. We know the pictures of the medieval alchemists—sinister, furtive figures in league with the devil. But they were not really; they were experimental research workers out of their time, sometimes misguided and always misrepresented because they were daring to question nature, against the injunctions of Saint Augustine against studying phenomena. "Go not out of doors," said Saint Augustine (354-430 A.D.). "Return into thyself. In the inner man dwells truth." Occasionally, men "went out of doors," like Roger Bacon, Duns Scotus and William of Ockham, all Franciscan friars in the thirteenth century, who insisted upon the principles of experimental science and applied them in experiments.

The alchemists were not wrong in thinking base metals can be turned into gold (as we know in these days of atomic transmutation), but they were liable to be witch-hunters because the Church had anathematized Democritus, who lived in the century before Plato (470-400 B.C.) and maintained (deductively) that everything was made up of atoms, including human beings, and that life was an interaction between atoms. In place of the elemental atoms of Democritus reigned Aristotle's four elements—earth, water, air and fire.

The Renaissance did not, of itself, bring about a release from this state of affairs. After the fall of Constantinople (1453) there was a great flood and ferment of scholarship, a new impetus to literature and to the fine arts and a great nostalgia for the Golden

Age of Greece. Refugees from the East brought Westwards fuller versions of the classical Greeks, like Plato and Aristotle, and also a great deal of new natural knowledge contributed by the Arabs. It was, however, a rediscovery of The Past and a rejection of novelty, and led to the decrying of the scientific approach of Duns Scotus to the extent that his name is now perpetuated in the word "dunce."

But other great ferments were at work. There was the invention of printing, the Great Navigations and the discovery of America. Practical science in the great "experiments" of travel was revealing facts about our world which were not in classical literature. Copernicus, Tycho Brahe, Kepler and Galileo were revealing facts about the heavens. Gilbert, personal physician to Queen Elizabeth, investigating the mariner's compass, had revealed magnetism and "that great magnet the earth"; it was an age of insurgent ideas, rebelling against the traditional science of two thousand years.

6. THE DAWN OF MODERN SCIENCE

SIR FRANCIS BACON (1561-1626) is generally accepted as "The Father of Modern Experimental Science" although, in fact, he never did any important experimental work, but he died as a result of an experiment when he went out at the age of sixty-five on a winter's day to stuff a goose with snow and contracted pneumonia. But his writings *The Proficience and Advancement of Learning, Novum Organum* and *New Atlantis* spell out the essentials of what are now accepted as the principles of modern science, rejecting the *deductive* or thinking-off-the-top-of-the-head principle and stating clearly the *inductive* or take-your-coat-off principle.

He insisted that the scientific man in the prosecution of his art of discovery has to practice three things: he must *observe* and choose his facts; he must form a *hypothesis* which links them together and provides a plausible explanation of them; he must carry out numerous and repeated *experiments* to prove, or disprove, his hypothesis.

That is the *Scientific Method* as we know it today. It is an exacting discipline which demands that a scientist lay aside all his prejudices (of which he has just as many as the rest of us); marshal his facts without fear or favor and frame his *hypothesis* on those facts, and then be prepared to labor for months or for years—just to prove himself wrong, perhaps, in the end. Claude Bernard, the dramatist, who became one of the world's greatest physiologists, gave this advice to all scientists:

> When you enter your laboratory, put off your imagination as you take off your coat; but put it on again, with your overcoat, when you leave. Before an experiment and between whiles let your imagination wrap you around; put it right away from you during the experiment itself lest it hamper you and your power of observation.

Bernard's remark applied to hypothesis-spinning, but it is valid if for "imagination," you read "politics," "religion," "prejudice" or any other preoccupation.

He gave another piece of advice which many, besides scientists, might heed:

> True science teaches to doubt, and, in ignorance, to refrain.

7. SCIENTIFIC LAWMAKING

LET US RECAPITULATE THROUGH A makeshift example how the Baconian principle works after three hundred years.

Suppose you are interested in animals and are pretty observant. You keep your eyes open and you notice all sorts of differences between animals—some have long tails and some have short, and some (to wit, human beings) have none at all. Some have toes, some have claws and some have hoofs. Some eat meat and some eat herbage. And so on. But you notice that a whole group of them including human beings, have one thing in common: they all suckle their young. So you call them "milk-giving animals," or if you know Latin you call them *mammals* (from the Latin word *mamma* meaning "female breast"). You observe them further and something strikes you as significant. None of those animals you have classified as mammals lay eggs. So on your *observations,* or known facts, you say: "Animals which suckle their young do not, apparently, lay eggs." That is a *hypothesis,* a provisional statement, on which you then proceed to do more research (notice the word "re-search" implying search and search again). You go around woods and farms and zoos and wherever you search you find that "animals which suckle their young do not lay eggs." You even find that there are fish or at least swimming animals like whales and seals which, unlike other fish, do not lay eggs but, by the same token, suckle their young. Now you are getting somewhere. Your *hypothesis* can be promoted to a *theory,* which is a *hypothesis* so well established that it has become respectable. You drop the word "apparently." But you are not satisfied. You travel through North America, South America, Europe, Africa and Asia observing and checking. Always it is the same: "Animals which suckle their young do not lay eggs." So now you think you can state it as a universal *law* of nature. You say: "No animals which suckle their young lay eggs." But since no scientific inquiry is ever complete, you go off again to the Australian continent, and there you meet the duck-billed platypus, or duck mole, that curious animal which not only *lays eggs* but also *suckles its young.* All that trouble just to prove yourself wrong in the end! But there is no need to throw yourself in the river. You can restate your *law* as "No animals (with the exception of, etc.) which suckle their young lay eggs." A scientific *law,* like a judicial law, defines the conditions in which it will apply. And, like modern law and unlike that of the Medes and Persians, a scientific law can be amended when new facts are brought to bear upon it.

*   *   *

This mutability of scientific *law* is important to remember; it is case law, not a dogma. It needs a great deal of supporting argument to get a scientific *law* amended, just as it needs a lot to amend the Constitution of the United States—but that is as it should be. And it contrasts the modern and the classical conception of science.

For instance, if you had asked an Aristotelian, "Why does an apple fall down and not up?" the concise reply would have been "An apple falls down but not up because it is its nature to fall down." There is no gainsaying that because it takes for granted that there is a divine ordinance which says to smoke, "Fly upwards" and to apples, "Fall downwards." It ascribes to objects *qualities* like "heaviness" or "lightness," just as men have qualities of "good" or "evil." But even then, the explanation is not wholly bad science; it does not suggest that a particular apple has a whim, at a particular moment, to fall down; it recognizes that all apples will fall down, not one, not a particular shape or color, nor a particular variety, but *all* apples. This ascribing of a common characteristic to a whole group of things (like your observation that there was a whole group of animals which suckled their young) is the basis of order in reasoning. And order is a prime essential in all scientific thought. Noticing differences is one thing. Noticing what they have in common is something else. For instance, primitive societies in some of the Pacific islands have a name for every tree but no word for "tree." To see what this means, imagine the predicament of a general who, instead of saying "The Fifty-first Division will attack at dawn," had to name every soldier in the division! So there is scientific merit in classification (even if it is just the word "apple") and a sufficient excuse for that tiresome habit of scientists, who continuously invent new words as labels for their packages of agreed facts.

But Sir Isaac Newton did not accept this Aristotelian idea of the "nature" of the apple. He noticed the apple fall, but he also knew of the experiments of Galileo, who had outraged then-existing ideas of "lightness" and "heaviness" by dropping (according to the now disputed legend) a one-pound weight and a hundred-pound weight from the top of the Leaning Tower of Pisa and proving that they reached the ground together; and of Tycho Brahe and the ellipses of the planets. And he worked out the Law of Gravitation and the Laws of Motion. He showed how any two masses attract each other—whether they be the sun and the earth or the earth and the apple—and that the force of the attraction is directly proportional to their masses and inversely proportional to the square of the distance between them. And how the planets spinning on their axes were held in their orbits, and their orbits pulled into ellipses by the interplay of these forces. And how the same laws which explained the motion of the heavenly bodies applied even to the corpuscles of matter—the atoms of Democritus.

Here was a body of universal law which could be tested by observation. It worked. Indeed, the results were so constant that Laplace, the great French mathematician, maintained that it was the final answer to all the processes of nature, past, present and future. Every particle, he maintained at the beginning of the nine-teenth century, must obey Newton's laws of motion, and if there was a brain big enough to do all the calculations, we could foretell the motion of every particle through all eternity. Here was *Certainty,* the unalterable process of *Cause* and *Effect.* Every result must have a cause and every cause a result, with a calculable certainty.

Since men are made up of atoms and our brains are made up of atoms, it would, on the Laplace argument, be possible to predict not only what my great-grandson will be doing at a given moment a hundred years from now, but what he would be thinking, just as surely as we can say that Halley's Comet will reappear in 1986.

Of course, Laplace's contention could never be put to the ultimate test, because no human brain and no electronic computer, however efficient, or vast, could do the calculation.

8. CERTAINTY IN THE NINETEENTH CENTURY

IT ILLUSTRATES, HOWEVER, THE COMPLETE FAITH which the nine-teenth century had in the Newtonian Laws. That faith created a sense of Scientific Predestination, of physical and unalterable processes leading inexorably from one event to the next. It affected social attitudes: Malthus predicted that the population would inevitably increase beyond the capacity of the soil to feed it, and this in turn produced the "inevitability of poverty," be-cause "obviously" if the condition of the poor were improved, by better sanitation or better food, they would live longer and have more children, and there would be less food so that their condi-tion would be worsened. It affected, of course, industry where mechanical behavior was self-evident: if the calculations were done properly, it was possible to predict how a machine would work. It affected politics in Karl Marx's Materialist Conception of His-tory, in which the cause of social and economic change is "powers of production," and the effect is a process by which one class is inevitably displaced by another. It colored, as Bronowski has pointed out, even the attitude of writers who began to see humanity struggling helplessly with Cause and Effect. Above all, it gave nineteenth-century scientists their cocksureness. Everything fitted into an orderly scheme of things—like Natural Selection, or the Periodic Table in which all the elements could be assembled, making ninety-two, and in which even those still undiscovered could not only be predicted but described (and they were so). Science was a train running on the rails of Certainty and it traveled far and fast.

* * *

But even the laws of Newton were not sacrosanct, although they were uncannily near perfection. A hundred years ago, the planet Uranus was not keeping time as it should. Two men, Adams in England, and Leverrier in France, working without knowledge of each other and merely with pencil and paper and the Laws of Gravitation, calculated that there must be a planet disturbing its gravitational force and where that planet must be. The great Berlin telescope was turned to the spot and there, sure enough, was the planet Neptune. This was a triumphant endorsement of the unalterable Laws of Gravitation. But sixty years later, astronomers searched in vain for the cause of similar discrepancies in the behavior of the planet Mercury, and we had to wait for Einstein and his Theory of Relativity to provide the explanation and modify the Laws of Newton.

9. HUMILITY IN THE TWENTIETH CENTURY

TWENTIETH-CENTURY SCIENTISTS are not so cocksure. Science today is much more modest. And one reason derives from the greatest advances which men have ever made—from the studies of the nucleus of the atom, which have produced the release of atomic energy. It is in the atom that we find *uncertainty* in a philosophically insoluble form. It is impossible to predict how an individual electron will behave. And it never will be possible; it is not a question of improving methods or instruments; it is unknowable.

No one, of course, has ever seen an individual atom or an electron. They have seen their effects in a cloud chamber or in the emulsion of a photographic plate—ionized trains. But the whole of the earth-shaking results of nuclear physics has followed from "models" which mean mental conceptions of the atom and its particles. These "models" derive from cause and effect—like

Rutherford's deduction that the cause of a beam of alpha particles being bent was the existence of a positively charged nucleus. But even in the early days when Bohr was trying to give theoretical explanations, he was bothered by the fact that Newtonian mechanics would not always fit, and he used them when they did and provided over explanations when they did not. His accommodating theories agreed beautifully with experimental observations. Science, however, does not like improvising laws and gradually new theories were systematized—like wave-mechanics and the quantum theory.

These explained a lot, but experimental evidence still depended on the *average* behavior of large numbers of particles, not on any one. From such statistical behavior, they could get a quite consistent picture and enable nuclear physics to advance to that apocalyptic moment of the explosion at Alamogordo.

*   *   *

That, however, does not satisfy the scientists. They want to know precisely what the position and velocity of any electron is. Only so can they predict what its path is likely to be. But they never can. Heisenberg, the German, who propounded the *Theory of Indeterminacy,* reasoned thuswise: if we want to know where an electron is we must illumine it with some kind of light (not necessarily visible ordinary light, but, say, X rays) and use a microscope (not any which we yet possess but one ideal for the purpose) and observe it, not with the unreliable human eye, but with a photographic plate or some other unbiased detector.

This involves using light, but light, with the wave lengths of visibility, would not serve. It would require X rays or even shorter gamma rays from radium. This would give *accuracy of position.* That is not enough; we cannot predict where Mars will be next Thursday unless we know the speed and direction in which it is traveling.

But (Heisenberg reasoned) if you use X rays or other intensive rays, they are so energetic that they will kick the electron forward or sideways. So you have changed its *speed* or its position at any moment and possibly its direction until you cannot be sure where it is going. What *The Theory of Indeterminacy,* or, *The Uncertainty Principle* boils down to is this: in the case of one electron, you can observe its *speed* at any moment, but you cannot know both speed and position simultaneously, which is what matters if you want to predict its future behavior. The mere act of observation changes the behavior.

We can understand that better from ordinary life. A teacher can never know for himself how his class behaves when he is out of the room, because when he comes back to look, the children behave quite differently. Or if someone says to me: "You behaved completely naturally on television last night," I know it is not true, because I knew I was being observed. I had arc lights beating down on me, as I do not normally have. I had a camera leering at me. I had the producer signaling to me. I had cramp from sitting in a prescribed position. I was behaving quite differently from what is normal for me.

10. CHANCE IS BACK

So THE SCIENTIST TODAY, instead of saying like Laplace, that if he knew at one instant the position and velocity of every particle in the universe, he would be able, in principle, to calculate everything that was going to happen, he says that, in principle, it is impossible to know at one instant the position and velocity of even a single particle.

Just as there was a tendency for people to take Laplace literally and reject uncertainty, so nowadays there are some who want to "throw out the baby with the bath water" and say that the Uncertainty Principle discredits Cause and Effect. Nothing of the sort. In the visible world, the physical principles still hold good and give precise, constantly checkable answers. But in the universe of the atom, it is no longer possible to say, "The certain behavior of a particle will be so and so." All that it is possible to say is that "From the observations of millions of particles, the probable behavior will be so and so."

So *Chance* is back. Probability is a perfectly valid scientific principle. And there are those, even among the exact scientists, who are relieved by it. Humility will do science no harm. "*Certainty*" with its sense of inevitability was one of the things which made ordinary people uneasy, if not afraid, of science.

PART

3

Great
Discoveries

. . . The success of a discovery depends upon the time of its appearance. . . .

SILAS WEIR MITCHELL

Great Discoveries (1)

1. THE METHOD, THE MAN, AND THE MOMENT

EDISON HAD OVER A THOUSAND PATENTS to his credit and only one scientific discovery. That one scientific discovery was the *Edison Effect,* which, by force of habit, he patented, but, as he himself said, he "did not have time to continue the experiment."

The discovery came about when he was developing the electric lamp, using a thread of carbon—made from Japanese bamboo—as the filament. Carbon, which is familiar to us as charcoal, graphite or diamond, has the peculiarity that when it is heated it passes into vapor. When, therefore, the filament (shaped like a hairpin) of the Edison lamp was too much heated, or "overrun," by a too high voltage, the carbon evaporated and condensed on the inner side of the tube and blackened it. But there was a clear streak, a "transparent shadow" in the blackening, in line with one of the legs of the carbon-loop of the filament. This showed that the carbon atoms were being shot off from the far leg of the loop and were bypassing the second leg. Edison made a guess at what was happening. He placed a metal plate between the two legs of the loop, connected a platinum wire to it and led the wire to the outside of the bulb. He then found that if he connected this wire, and a lead from the intake terminal, to a sensitive detector (a galvanometer), he got a definite current flowing. But if he attached a lead from the outlet terminal, connected to the leg which was casting the shadow, he got no response. That meant that there was a current flowing in one direction only, like traffic down a one-way street.

Edison never satisfactorily explained the effect, because he was too busy inventing other things, and he, who made such good use of other people's scientific facts, did not realize the significance of his own.

But we do today. Our world-wide communications, our broadcasting systems, our amplifiers, our television, our talkies, all depend on the Edison Effect. It is the explanation of the vacuum tube and of the amplifying tube. But the meaning of Edison's discovery of 1884 was not realized until 1904, when Ambrose Fleming, in Britain, patented the thermionic valve. Notice the word "valve." Fleming gave it that name because here was a device which allowed negative electricity to flow from the filament to the tube, but not the other way. It is like the valves in the veins of our bodies, which allow the blood in them to move only toward the heart, or like the valve in the auto tire which allows the air to go in but not to come out. By inserting a "trap," Fleming found that the effect could be used to rectify and detect radio waves. Lee De Forest, the American, by adding a third factor, the "grid," completed the invention of the modern radio valve.

* * *

This story of a great and observant mind which, for once, missed the point, illustrates the essentials of a great discovery. A great discovery depends on three things—*The Method, The Man* and *The Moment. The Method* is what was discussed in Part Two— the observation, followed by the hypothesis or shrewd guess, followed by experiments to test the validity of the guess; the theory, which is the guess now justified by these experiments; and the further tests which keep on confirming the validity of the experiments and the theory. *The Man* implies someone with the gift of acute observation. *The Moment* is that incident in time, or the scientific "climate," in which a whole lot of circumstances combine to make the discovery possible. And in that order, because if *The Man* does not have *The Method,* he will miss *The Moment.*

Edison did not have a scientific training, in the sense of schooling. But you do not have to have a license to use the method. It is a system of thought, a habit of mind, and in Edison's case, largely an intuitive approach. He was a self-taught "methodist." He was certainly "The Man," the gifted individual with shrewd insight, spotting an idea which others had missed and following it through.

The Moment in the case of the Edison Effect had not arrived. It had to wait for J. J. Thomson's discovery of the electron in 1897. Before that, in 1879, Sir William Crookes had shown the existence of cathode rays. Thomson took up their investigation. "I had for a long time been convinced," he wrote later, "that these rays were charged particles, but it was some time before I had any suspicion that they were anything but charged atoms. My first doubts to this being the case were aroused when I measured the deflection of the rays by a magnet, for this was far greater than I could account for by any hypothesis, which seemed at all reasonable if the particles had a mass at all approaching that of the hydrogen atom, the smallest then known."

This experiment showed that his particles must be only about 1/1840th of the mass of hydrogen atoms and that they were traveling with velocities of some 1,500 kilometers a second. He first called them "corpuscles," which conveyed the idea that electricity was not a continuous intangible something, but the swarming of infinitesimal specks. In fact, he and Rutherford strained them out by passing them through tubes filled with cotton wool, as the pips are strained out of raspberry jelly by the jelly bag. With the recognition of the nature of electrons, Ambrose Fleming in 1904 reached The Moment when he could explain something which had eluded Edison twenty years before.

*   *   *

This discussion of Edison implies that there are two different animals—the scientist and the inventor. In modern practice, the distinction seems real and we go further: we think of a whole series of "castes" in science—the "pure" scientist, the "fundamental applied" scientist, the "inventor," the "applied" scientist, the "technologist" and the "technician." The pure scientist we think of as someone like Einstein, concerned only with theory, or Rutherford asking, "Why do these rays come off Marie Curie's radium?" (without thinking about the future release of atomic energy). The fundamental applied scientist is someone who works out, say, the behavior of metals, so that eventually people can develop the special steels of a jet engine. The inventor is the man who, knowing that sort of thing, has the idea of how they might be practically applied. The applied scientist is the man who is set a specific problem for which he has to find a specific answer. He is the man who studies, not the behavior of gases in general, but how gas will behave in a jet engine. The technologist is the man who develops the "know-how" and shows how scientific ideas can be made to "work for their living" in an industrial process. The technician is the man who makes them work.

Some people would say that these divisions are artificial and in fact a kind of snobbery, that pure science, however immaculate and remote it may seem from practical application, ultimately has some functional value, that Einstein's $E=mc^2$, which when expressed as "potential energy equals mass multiplied by the square of the speed of light" sounds completely academic and unpractical, eventually explodes at Alamogordo as an atomic bomb, and that the skill of the technician is only in a different degree the trained acumen of the academic scientist. Perhaps today the clue is the word "degree." We have classified the practitioners of science by their qualifications and by labels which we attach, usually in the form of university degrees or diplomas in this or that; or, in the technician level, by craft distinctions.

But great discoveries have not been confined to the nineteenth or twentieth century, when this pattern of science and technology came into being. We are the heirs of the many great discoveries whose discoveries are lost in the anonymity of history and, indeed, of prehistory.

2. THE UNKNOWN DISCOVERERS

BENJAMIN FRANKLIN DESCRIBED MAN, or *Homo sapiens,* as a "tool-making animal." Somewhere in the history of mankind that agglomeration of brain cells which we might call the conscious mind and will of Man, made a great discovery. Man found that he, naked and defenseless against beasts which could attack and kill him with tooth and claw, could protect himself by attaching a stone to a stick which was sufficiently long, not only to keep him away from his enemy, but to give it a swing which would increase its force. And then he learned to clothe his nakedness in the skins of his enemy.

At what stage in history did Man discover fire? We can imagine the Peking Man or the Javanese Man (unless we accept the legend of Prometheus stealing fire from the gods) making a great discovery half a million years ago. Perhaps Primitive Man saw a tree set on fire by lightning, and, overcoming his elemental fears, seized a burning branch and set fire to other wood and kept his manmade fire alight, until at some later stage he discovered that he could produce a spark and a fire at will. Or maybe it was the boy-scout way of rubbing two pieces of wood together.

At what stage in history did Man discover he could make his food more appetizing by roasting it with fire? Perhaps it was like Charles Lamb's story of the Chinese whose house caught fire and burned his pigs; and when he touched the roast pig, burned his fingers and stuck them in his mouth and sucked them, he discovered how tasty it was. And when he wanted more roast pig, he built houses and burned them and the pigs in them until he discovered it was not really necessary to go to such extremes.

At what stage in history did Man discover that, with his superior brain power, he did not need to hunt animals but could husband them and domesticate them? When did he discover the virtues of grain and that he could plant it and cultivate it? When did he discover that he could smelt metals and shape them into weapons and tools? Was there that moment, before even the days of the Assyrians, when people, burning a fierce fire on the sands, found that they had produced glass? They were not to know that it was a fusion of silica with metallic oxide, but they did know that with certain sands and with fire they could go on producing glass.

When did Man discover that instead of drying clay mud in the sun he could bake it in ovens and make hard bricks or pottery?

Another great discovery of which we do not know the origin is the wheel. This was one of the greatest departures in human thinking. Everything mechanical up to this point had been an extension of the human limbs. The cave man's club was an extra fist on an extra forearm. The broadened mattock was a version of his fingers, formed like a scoop, with which he had first scratched the soil. And so on.

To move anything implied some sort of motion like that of the human limbs. To think of something rotating meant getting away from the human analogy. The lever and fulcrum by which it was found that weights could be moved by using a long pole resting on a rock was the first stage. Great blocks of stone, like those used to build the Pyramids, could be shifted by resting them on logs and levering the blocks along, the logs turning in the process.

Then somebody separated the weight-carrying properties of the log from the rotating properties, as the fixed axle and the turning wheel. That was a revolutionary idea in more senses than one. It was the forerunner, thousands of years ago, of the twentieth-century preoccupation with the rotary movement. We are now moving away from the arm movement, the piston drive, which James Watt embodied in his steam engine and which continued in the piston movement of the internal-combustion engine. Now we think of turbines, where the steam or hot gases act directly on the blades of the turbine as the water acted on the blades of the water wheel.

It is salutary to remind ourselves that we are very late with this development because the first of all steam engines was that of Hero of Alexandria a hundred and forty years before the Christian era, and was a jet-propelled turbine. The basis of this was a sphere of metal with two right-angle tubes set in it, with the outlets pointing in opposite directions like the arms of a swastika. There was a boiler from which the steam entered the sphere and, escaping through the angular tubes, forced the sphere to swirl round on its axis. Incidentally, Hero knew how to make a little effort go a long way. He knew how, by a screw operating on a toothed cogwheel winding a cord over a series of pulleys, he could make a lever lift a weight out of all proportion to the muscular strength of the person turning the screw. This was the early gearing principle.

Man learned to harness the wind and the water. He found that the force of a rush of water could turn a wheel. He found that a sail could, with a favorable wind, move a ship as effectively as the muscle drag on oars. Somewhere, probably in China, someone discovered that if you fitted sails on an axle they would rotate and produce a windmill.

There were the other great discoveries like the invention of numbers and the letters of the written language, and of block printing, as we find, for example, in the *Book of Chou Pei Suan King* about 1000 B.C., twenty-five hundred years before printing appeared in Europe. There was the discovery of paper which took the place of clay tablets and skins, and the great cosmic discoveries, like the charting of the stars.

All these great anonymous discoveries, usually from quite workaday origins—like the need for measurement because, as was mentioned in Part Two, the Nile when it flooded wiped out normal landmarks and demanded the science of surveying—, are part of the heritage which is embodied in that orderly assembly of knowledge which is called science.

3. SOCIAL INFLUENCE ON DISCOVERY

SCIENCE AND DISCOVERY, while they have helped to shape civilization, are not something apart from these civilizations. There is, as has been emphasized, The Moment. It belongs not only to the stage of scientific thinking but to the conditions in which that scientific thinking is being done. Hero's steam engine remained a scientific curiosity, an amusing toy, because he lived in a slave civilization, in which there was abundant manpower and no need for a substitute for muscle. Indeed, it has been argued that the construction of the Pyramids in the days of the Pharaohs was an enormous piece of public works, an Egyptian form of WPA, because there was an unemployed slave population; and work, rather than soldiers, was the best way of keeping them quiet.

Or the moment may depend on a combination of circumstances, like things being discovered for quite different reasons, making the fulfillment of a new discovery possible. If we look at Leonardo da Vinci's fantastic record of frustrated inventions, we will see what is meant by that. His airplane, aerodynamically practical, could not work because the only available motive power was muscle, and so man's flight had to wait for the discovery of gasoline and the compact internal-combustion engine. Although it is said that Leonardo abandoned his idea of the submarine because it was too dangerous to put in the hands of irresponsible men, it obviously could not reach fulfillment until there was power-drive in other forms than muscle, and until we understood the nature of oxygen and the metabolic processes. This knowledge enabled us to devise means of keeping men functioning out of direct contact with the air they normally breathe. People flirted with the idea of motion pictures, but they became possible not as a principle but as a fact when chemists discovered that wood could be turned into celluloid. Francis Bacon might have had the right ideas when he, in effect, committed suicide, by going out on a winter's day (and catching pneumonia) to stuff a goose with snow. But practical refrigeration and "deep freeze" had to wait, not only for the theoretical explanations of exchange of heat, but for the solution of the practical engineering problems which came from the nineteenth-century experience of engineering for purposes other than refrigeration. Jet propulsion was not possible until the 1930's because, even if the theoretical principles were quite clear, we had to wait for the metallurgists working on steels for quite different reasons to produce those which would stand the extremely high heat and pressures.

* * *

There are periods when the advance of science practically stands still—as in the Dark Ages—because the philosophy of the times is hostile to it, or those in power discourage it (although we must not forget that the invention of gunpowder and the cannon was the beginning of the end of the feudal system).

There are periods when science becomes stagnant because the atmosphere is too complacent. The great scientific outburst of the seventeenth century, identified with Newton and his contemporaries, flagged. From 1690 to 1750 there was a period of relative decline. Some might say that it was a period of consolidation, the time needed to digest the banquet of new ideas, but it was also a period of postprandial lassitude, when men had a nap after their meal and largely forgot the great work of the seventeenth century. Science became a leisured class diversion. The landed gentry and the merchants had been too prosperous. They took up science, but it was a plaything of which they soon got tired. The Royal Society itself revived only with the transfusion of vulgar blood and urgent ideas, which came in with the Industrial Revolution. It revived when men like Benjamin Franklin, the printer, Matthew Boulton, the toy maker, James Watt, the university mechanic, Priestley, the Unitarian minister, and indeed most of the members of The Lunar Society became Fellows. For example, Wedgwood, the potter, was elected a Fellow of The Royal Society on the strength of his paper on "The Pyrometer or Heat Measuring Instrument." It dealt with a thermometer devised to withstand the temperatures at which glass melts. It was entirely a functional paper concerned with the determination of the degree of baking required for different qualities of earthenware and china products, but it involved new principles.

The universities had sunk in the eighteenth century to a state of intellectual ineptitude and bigotry. Their place was taken by the new centers largely identified with industry, like the Philadelphia Academy, founded by Franklin, and similar institutions founded in Manchester, Birmingham and Glasgow, and by the setting up of the Royal Institution in London by Count Rumford.

*   *   *

Count Rumford was a fascinating man. He was an American, Benjamin Thompson, who had first been on the side of the colonists in the Revolutionary War, but had deserted to the British and become an Under Secretary of State for the Colonies. He later offered his services to the King of Bavaria, who made him a count of the Holy Roman Empire. As Count Rumford he returned to London and promoted the idea of setting up, by private subscription, "an establishment for feeding the poor and giving them useful employment . . . connected with an institution for bringing forward into general use new inventions and improvements, particularly such as relate to the management of heat and the saving of fuel and to various other mechanical contrivances, by which domestic comfort and economy may be promoted." To that end the Royal Institution was formed with the further object of "teaching by regular courses of philosophic lectures and experiments; the application of the new discoveries in science to the improvement of arts and manufactures; and in facilitating the means of procuring the comforts and conveniences of life." The emphasis changed very quickly—from preoccupation with the problems of the poor to a concern for the kind of discoveries which could promote industrial advantage—but the Institution did provide the laboratory for Sir Humphrey Davy, in the first instance, and for Faraday, and a long succession of famous scientists.

*   *   *

As one of the earliest examples of Lend-Lease and reverse Lend-Lease, it is interesting to compare the foundation of the Royal Institution with that of the Smithsonian Institution in Washington. Thompson was a renegade American. Smithson was a rebel Englishman. Smithson was the illegitimate son of Sir Hugh Smithson, a coal magnate, who became the first Duke of Northumberland. Sir Hugh had married the heiress of the Percy's, the traditional Earls of Northumberland, and to his own coal estates in Yorkshire he had added her large estates in Northumberland, another great coal field. His wealth was fabulous. His eldest legitimate son, who became the second Duke, fought against the Americans at Lexington, but an illegitimate son was born to him and to a widow, Mrs. Macie, in 1765. She was the niece of the Duke of Somerset and descended from Henry VII through Lady Jane Grey, and was herself wealthy. The Duke, while admitting paternity, would not publicly recognize his illegitimate son, who was entered at Oxford in the name of Macie, but took the name of Smithson in 1802. A brilliant chemist, he was made a Fellow of The Royal Society at the age of twenty-two, one of his sponsors being the legendary Henry Cavendish, the hermit scientist. Smithson had the Oedipus complex to a spectacular degree. He hated his father and loathed his stepbrothers, the Percys of Northumberland. He refused to take any share of his father's great wealth, but he had inherited a fortune from his mother. This passed into the hands of the Government of the United States in 1837. James Smithson never went to the United States, although he had been brought up in France and had been sympathetic both to the Americans in the Revolutionary War and to the Jacobins in the French Revolution. He willed that his fortune should go to set up an institution to be called "Smithsonian" as an establishment for the increase and diffusion of knowledge among men. But his object was less concerned with science than with sublimated revenge. He wrote, "The best blood of England flows in my veins. On my father's side I am a Northumberland. On my mother's, I am related to kings, but this avails me not. Yet my name shall live in the memory of man when the titles of the Northumberlands and the Percys are extinct and forgotten." And his boast may well be justified.

4. THE CLIMATE OF DISCOVERY

THERE WAS IN THE HISTORY of both the Royal Institution and the Smithsonian Institution a classic example of this discussion of The Moment. Michael Faraday, blacksmith's son and bookbinder's apprentice, who had succeeded Sir Humphrey Davy at the Royal Institution, and Joseph Henry, the first head of Smithsonian, were contemporaries. It is clear from Faraday's diaries and from Henry's accounts of his experiments with parallel wires that they were both flirting with electromagnetic induction, to wit, radio, and both Faraday's papers on *Thoughts on Ray-Vibrations* and Henry's deduction between the similarity of the spreading of electrical disturbance were the forerunners of Clerk-Maxwell's electromagnetic theory of light and of Hertz's demonstration that radio waves and light waves differ in wave length only. So they might be described as the joint parents of the radio, but the world had to wait another sixty years for their practical fulfillment. The year 1832 was not The Moment.

*　　*　　*

There is, therefore, a give-and-take between science and social conditions. It is an interaction; science helps to create the social conditions; social conditions recharge the accumulators of science. To try to isolate them and imply that science is somehow immune from social and economic forces is absurd. But neither is it justifiable to say that all developments of science are dictated by this interplay of forces. There is a general climate in which science as a whole flourishes, and in which certain definite trends grow. But the history of science is full of examples, where, like a mutation appearing in biology, a new "strain" of science appears, concerned more with the personality of the scientist than with the impulses of his time.

One of the perfect examples of this is Hopkins and butterfly wings. Sir Frederick Gowland Hopkins was the "father" of biochemistry in Britain, one of the world's greatest scientists, and was awarded the Nobel Prize for his pioneer work on vitamins. Hopkins as a boy was a lonely little chap who used to chase butterflies around the hedgerows of Enfield on the outskirts of London. He had a definite scientific urge, but he started off his career in the insurance world. At the age of seventeen he wrote his first "scientific paper," a letter to the *Entomologist*. It was on the bombardier beetle. He had noticed that this insect, when disturbed, ejected a violent vapor into the air. He put specimens in a test tube and encouraged them to shoot. The vapor condensed on the side of the tube, and he collected the material. "I think," he wrote later, "that from that time my fate was sealed. Though the designation was not yet invented, I became there and then a biochemist at heart." He remained fascinated by insects, particularly butterflies. When a small inheritance helped him to take up science and to enter it the hard way, he kept his interest in butterflies. In 1889, at the age of twenty-eight, having "learned his trade," he started to work on the pigments of butterfly wings, and in 1896, while he was working at Guy's Hospital as an assistant to a specialist in forensic medicine (and, as such, taking part in the leading crime investigations of the day), he presented a paper to The Royal Society on the pigments of butterfly wings.

He showed that the opaque white of butterfly wings was uric acid and that the yellow of a wing was a related substance which can be produced when uric acid is heated under pressure. (This observation on butterflies turned his attention to the uric acid problems of man.) And he kept on reverting to butterfly wings until at the age of eighty, at the end of a great career in which he had become the President of The Royal Society, President of the British Association, Nobel-Prize winner and a member of the rare Order of Merit, he delivered his last paper on butterfly wings. Of all his great contributions to science, this fascination with buterflies, about which some of his eminent colleagues had been pitying and derisive, had by then become one of the most significant. For it had been found that the pigments were not simple uric acid derivatives, but belonged to a group of compounds now called "pterins" (from the Greek word for "wing"). Pterin is the base of folic acid; it is the base of at least some of the factors which cause cancer; and it figures in the pyramidine group, which is a constituent of nucleic acid—that is, of the innermost chemistry of the cells which make up the living body and in which ultimately resides the secret of Life itself. That is the privilege and value of the pure scientist, that he can chase a will-o'-the-wisp, and prove it to be CH_4, or chase a butterfly and be led into the heart of the living cell!

No one was more aware of his day and generation, no one more conscious of the social circumstances of his time or more insistent that the scientist does not exist in an ivory tower than Gowland Hopkins. But it is "stretching it a bit" to suggest that it was the external forces of his time which kept Hopkins chasing butterflies throughout a long and scientifically eventful life.

*   *   *

Nevertheless, great discoveries are never accidents. Some may be called intuitive, but that is only saying that in the flash of a clear-thinking mind something which others have missed has become plain. What are commonly called accidents are usually, as Pasteur said, the impact of an *observed fact on a prepared mind.* But a precondition is that the mind should be *prepared,* that either by education or experience the observer should have acquired the capacity for logical thought and mental discipline. That is what distinguishes the rational being who asks "Why?" when observing some phenomenon from the superstitious being who accepts it as something supernatural and not to be questioned. You may accept lightning as a Jovian thunderbolt, or you may, like Benjamin Franklin, knowing something about electricity, regard it as a discharge of atmospheric electricity, and send up a kite to prove it.

A great discovery may be something eminently practical, even though it may not be self-evidently so. For example, when the British statesman Mr. W. E. Gladstone asked Michael Faraday what useful purpose his electromagnetic induction would have, the reply was, "Sir, you may be able to tax it." Which is another version of Franklin's reply, when asked what was the value of a new idea. He retorted, "What is the use of a new-born child?"

When the practical value is self-evident, we usually call it an "invention." Sometimes a great discovery is entirely theoretical, like Newton's discovery of Gravitation, or like Einstein's Theory of Relativity; and sometimes it is apocalyptic, like the explosion of the first atomic bomb at Alamogordo. That was a "discovery" because, although it was theoretically implicit in the work of the nuclear physicists, no one was sure until that moment at 5:30 A.M. on Monday, July 16, 1945, whether such a release of energy was in fact practicable.

5. THE MAKERS-POSSIBLE AND THE MAKERS-TO-HAPPEN

ONE OF THE MOST FUTILE OF OCCUPATIONS is deciding claims and counterclaims for this or that discovery. It is possible to date patents or priorities, but these are usually only the manifestations of a great deal of work done by a great many people. It is like a coral reef, built up through the ages out of the deposits of myriads of organisms, and the only ones visible are those which, on the foundations of dead generations, bring a reef above the surface of the sea.

Every discovery has a pedigree, and the pedigrees of some are as complicated as the family trees of the princely families of the *Almanach de Gotha*. But let us be quite clear: a discovery is certainly not spontaneous generation, nor, like Minerva, does it spring fully armed from the brain of Jupiter. It is further complicated, when we begin to examine chronological claims, by the fact that there does exist a *scientific climate*.

In the ferment which followed the announcement of Hahn and Strassman, working in Berlin, they had found that by bombarding uranium with neutrons they were left with barium, which showed that the atom was splitting into two different parts.

In Copenhagen, Frisch, working on the theories of his aunt, Lise Meitner, as to the significance of Hahn's discovery, found that the particles were traveling apart with energies of one hundred million volts, far greater than anything yet produced artificially on earth. The experiment was confirmed immediately, at Columbia University, Carnegie Institution, Johns Hopkins and the University of California.

But even that was not so remarkable as, for example, the fact that Rutherford, as a student working in the cloakroom of Canterbury College. New Zealand, in 1894, improvised a radio detector consisting of a coil of wire wound round a bundle of fine sewing needles in combination with a small magnet. This was a method which Joseph Henry had used in 1842, but Rutherford knew nothing about Henry's work, nor did he know at the same moment another young man, Marconi, had done a similar thing. Rutherford submitted his detector to The Royal Society; Marconi, with commercial foresight, sent his specifications to the Patents Office. Again that was not as uncanny as Faraday and Henry three thousand miles apart with no exchange and no communication and no common reference working out, almost identically, electromagnetic induction.

*　*　*

There is one way to distinguish the areas of responsibility for a discovery, that is between *The Makers-Possible* and *The Makers-to-Happen*. The Makers-Possible include the "ancestors" whose work was inherited by the particular generation of discovery, and those whose theoretical or academic work brings the saturated solution of knowledge to the point of crystallization. The Makers-to-Happen are those who, whether you call them applied scientists or inventors or technologists, bring the idea to a practical achievement. The Makers-Possible are those who say "Why?" and The Makers-to-Happen those who say "How?"

Great Discoveries (2)

1. IRÈNE HAS FIFTEEN TEETH

ON OCTOBER 17, 1898, MARIE CURIE MADE A NOTE: "Irène can walk very well and no longer goes on all fours."

On January 6, 1899, she made an entry: "Irène has 15 teeth."

Between these two entries there was another note: "We believe that the new radioactive substance contains a new element to which we propose to give the name RADIUM."

Irène, whose fifteenth tooth was as noteworthy, to her mother, as a new scientific discovery, was, like her, to become a famous scientist and, again like her mother, to win the Nobel Prize. The fact that such simple domestic events, like a teething baby or a successful recipe for gooseberry jelly, were important to Marie Curie in the year of her great discoveries of the new elements polonium and radium is also important to a sympathetic understanding of science.

*   *   *

While it is proper that we should honor great achievements and appreciate the romance of science, it is unfortunate, and indeed damaging to science, when we forget that scientists are in fact human beings. If we can think of them in life-size and as normal biological specimens, and not as disembodied brains, we can see their achievements in their real perspective; awe-struck reverence of the Scientific Mind is as irrational and, indeed, as superstitious, as the awesome fear that the pagan Dyaks have of Jabu, the Spirit of the Mountain.

People cannot understand scientists or science if they imagine that they belong to a different order of thinking or of being from themselves. Nor is it good for scientists to think of themselves as a sort of race apart, with a special dispensation of a peculiar intelligence. The really great ones never do. Madame Curie has her justifiable place in history as one of the greatest scientists and the greatest women. Her discovery of radium, apart from the humanitarian benefits it conferred, opened the doors to the stupendous atomic developments of the twentieth-century (and surely, in this instance, an adjective like "stupendous" is justifiable). But radium, and its radioactive significance, was not a fortuitous discovery—it was an incident, albeit a momentous one, in the progress of physical discovery.

*   *   *

The Germans Pluecker and Hittorf, between 1850 and 1870, had studied the passage of electricity through gases at low pressure, and another German, Goldstein, had given the name "cathode rays" to something traveling in straight lines from the cathode (the negative electric pole) to the walls of a container. Sir William Crookes developed a tube shaped like an airship. At the narrow end he set his cathode. Toward the bulbous end he set, as his anode or positive pole, a metal cross. When the current was switched on, something was beamed from the cathode which made the glass at the other end glow, and there was no doubt that the "something" proceeded in straight lines because the obstructing cross cast a clean-cut shadow. Crookes thought the "something" must be a form of light, but, when he brought a magnet near the tube, he found that the beam was bent out of its path, suggesting that there must be a stream of material particles.

This "something" was neither solid, liquid nor gas, so he described it as a "Fourth State of Matter."

2. THOSE NAUGHTY, NAUGHTY RAYS

Sixteen years later, in 1895, we find the wife of a not-very-well-known professor of physics, at the University of Würzburg, in Bavaria, being very cross with her husband.

Frau Roentgen, as a wife and housewife, had some justification. Wilhelm was late for dinner, as he had been for the past few days. He had been very strange—absentminded and unsociable and untidy. His wife, trying to humor him in his strange mood, had been all afternoon in the steaming kitchen making his favorite meal, and not only had he risked spoiling it by being late, but now he did not even seem to be aware that he was eating it. So she was really cross, and contritely—for Wilhelm was not a bad husband—he explained that he really was worrying about something and, to appease her, he took her across to his laboratory to see the "something."

So Frau Roentgen was the first person, apart from her husband, to see the phenomenon of X rays. Her reaction is not recorded, but probably she thought it was not much justification for the wasted meal—just some salts glowing in the pitch-darkness of the laboratory.

But to the trained mind of her husband—the Man with the Method—that glow was profoundly significant. For some time he had been experimenting with a vacuum tube, trying to explain, as Crookes had not done, the behavior of the particles. He had been studying the effects of fluorescent salts, which glow in response to certain light waves. As a check for one of his experiments, he had enclosed a tube in blackened cardboard, so completely shutting in all light. Then (November 8, 1895) he noticed the salts lying twelve feet away from the tube, glowing in the darkness. Very queer! This was against all the rules. There must be some invisible "light" coming from the dark lantern.

Years later he was asked by the famous heart specialist Sir James Mackenzie what he thought when he noticed it. "Thought!" said the scientist. "I did not think. I investigated!"

He checked and rechecked for the explanation. He put a dense object on top of a sealed wooden box in which he enclosed a photographic plate, and, exposing it to the unseen rays, he got an image on the plate. He could photograph the skeleton of his own hand. If the pressure in the tube was low enough, he could get the bones without barely a shadow of the flesh. Or he could photograph the money in a purse without the image of the purse itself. This was "pure" research—the study of a natural phenomenon for its own sake—but Roentgen, from the outset, saw its practical significance in surgery; and that was why the first paper on Roentgen rays was read to the Medical Society of Würzburg. It was he who called them X rays, because they were an "unknown quantity," and perhaps that was why the public seized on them with sensational avidity. The layman did not properly understand, and a great deal of amusing confusion arose.

A contemporary doggerel ran:

"I am full of daze,
Shock and amaze,
For nowadays
I hear they'll gaze
Through cloak and gown—and even stays,
These naughty, naughty Roentgen rays."

In America the Purity League proposed legislation to prevent the use of X rays in opera glasses in theaters, and enterprising stores made money out of selling X-ray proof corsets and modesty gowns. Even today, more than half a century later, some people are still obsessed with the idea of a Peeping Tom with X-ray eyes. But these ideas are all wrong. X rays can only produce shadows. They cast a shadow which a photographic plate can "fix," or which you can see on a special screen. But they do not reflect back images onto the eye as ordinary light does when it enables us to see things.

3. THE ELECTRIC PIPS

BUT THE POPULAR SENSATION was scarcely greater than the sensation which the announcement caused amongst scientists. To the physicists, this was the beginning of a new attack on the secrets of nature. They did not know the nature of the rays, but they knew they were something different from Crookes's "material particles." They recognized that they were coming from the bombardment of the metal plate by cathode rays.

Professor J. J. Thomson seized on it immediately and had the Roentgen experiments reproduced at the Cavendish Laboratory, Cambridge. One of the "boys" whom he put onto the work was a young newcomer from New Zealand, named Ernest Rutherford. Among the things they discovered was that gases, when treated with X ray, became conductors of electricity. This was useful because it helped them to use small voltages in their study of gases, whereas hitherto they had had to use high voltages which overheated the apparatus and caused flames and sparks. Thomson and Rutherford, studying these X-radiated gases, found that when they were passed through tightly packed cotton wool, the gases ceased to conduct electricity. Like pips being strained out of raspberry jelly through a muslin bag, electric "pips" were being strained out of the gases! "Something" which had been moving in the gases had been removed. Following up this, and other experiments, J. J. Thomson announced the discovery of the electron in 1897.

4. THE URANIUM MYSTERY

SIMILARLY IN FRANCE, X RAYS had caused scientific excitement. Jules Henri Poincaré, the famous mathematical physicist, formed the hypothesis—made an inspired guess—that X rays or rays similar to them might be given off by fluorescent salts—that is, by chemicals which glow under the action of light, like those with which Roentgen had been experimenting.

This idea appealed to Antoine Henri Becquerel, professor of

physics at the Museum of Natural History in Paris. He prepared salts of an odd element, uranium. This element was just a laboratory curiosity. It had been taken for granted that its fluorescence was caused by the action of light upon it. Becquerel, however, did with this chemical what Roentgen had done with the cathode tube; he cut out the light factor altogether by wrapping it in black paper. He placed this on silver foil on top of a photographic plate. The plate was blotched where the salts had been, showing that they had given off rays which were strong enough to penetrate the lightproof paper and the silver foil. As a careful experimenter, he had to guard against the possibility that the salts were in fact stores of light—that is to say, that they had been activated by light and were reacting slowly. He kept them in darkness for months, but still they gave off these rays. Maybe Poincaré had been right, and they might be giving off X rays. Here again he applied careful tests which showed they had no more in common than they had with light-stimulated fluorescence. It was then obvious to the trained mind that the rays were spontaneously generated by uranium itself, which was continuously giving off these rays in the same way as the sun dispenses the energy which we call sunlight.

Becquerel had discovered—and gave us the word—radioactivity. He announced this important truth within a year of the discovery of X rays.

5. RADIUM

MARIE SKLODOWSKA WAS A MEMBER of the Polish underground. Yes, there was a Polish underground in the 1890's, a resistance movement against the Czars who had set out to destroy the Polish nation and to Russianize it. Her father was a teacher and he taught her to be a Pole. She acquired her interest in science in the Floating University in Warsaw, a furtive, clandestine gathering of Polish resistance. In this underground movement there were research laboratories for learning and teaching science, which the Czars denied to the poor. She became a governess, and with her meager savings she crossed Europe in a fourth-class railway carriage—a horse truck—and enrolled herself at the Paris Sorbonne to starve her way through a degree.

In Paris she met and married the poorly paid chief of the laboratory of the School of Physics and Chemistry, Pierre Curie. Pierre, with his brother Jacques, had in his early twenties discovered the important phenomenon "piezo electricity," an effect which depends on the behavior of certain crystals so that they can be made to act like an electric tuning fork. Not only does the application of this effect provide a useful laboratory instrument for measurement, but today quartz crystals act as the traffic policeman of the ether, as the precise controllers of radio wave-bands.

With that major discovery to his credit and with fifteen years' service as a college teacher, Pierre was earning as much as a skilled factory worker when he, at the age of thirty-six, married Marie Sklodowska, age twenty-eight.

In the year of Becquerel's discovery, 1897, Marie had given birth to a daughter, Irène, the future Nobel-Prize winner, and while she kept house, bathed the baby and scrubbed pans, she pondered on how she could get her doctor's degree. She studied Becquerel's results and made her own hypothesis, which was a revolutionary one—that the strange radiations were in fact particles coming out of the atom. Here was an idea which went against all the classical arguments of the atoms of Democritus—even against the name itself, since "atom" means *indivisible*—and against the "corpuscles" of Newton. But that hypothesis would be difficult prove if such a radiation was merely a feeble peculiarity of uranium. Did other elements behave the same way?

Then began a search which is one of the great epics of science, not only because it gave us radium, but because it is an example of persistence and endurance. With the primitive equipment of her husband's laboratory, she began examining *every known element*. Presently she found another, thorium, which had the same radioactive properties as uranium. Then, not content with testing elements in the pure stage or in simple compounds, she started testing minerals in which, in nature, these elements were bound up. She got chunks of everything she could lay her hands on, and among them she found some which gave radiations stronger than uranium or thorium—notably pitchblende from Bohemia (suggested to her by Becquerel). This contained uranium, but also something more powerful. Since she had already examined every known element, it must be a new element. Eminent scientists told her not to be so silly, but her husband aided and abetted her.

What led to confusion was that in looking for one powerful element the Curies were unwittingly on the trail of two. By July, 1898, they had isolated one of them. Before it was even announced to the French Academy, Marie sent a copy of her manuscript to the clandestine "Floating University" in Warsaw for publication. As a defiant act of resistance she called the new element *Polonium* after the Poland which Czarist Russia denied existed.

Six months later, when Irène had fifteen teeth, she was affirming the existence of a second new element—*Radium*. It took another four years to produce it in experimental quantities—four years of working in an unheated, unventilated shed, over boiling caldrons of pitchblende, stirred with a metal rod as big as herself. The result was a tenth of a gram. On the night of their final achievement the Curies went back to the shed after dark and there, in the ramshackle interior, were blue glowworms, the radiant halo produced by one of the world's greatest and most beneficial discoveries.

Radium became one of the world's most precious and costly substances. The Curies could have been wealthy if, instead of freely disclosing their discovery, they had patented their method. They had a Canadian offer but decided not to take it, and, having renounced the chance of a fortune, they got on their bicycles and pedaled happily to the woods of Clamart.

6. INTO THE ATOM

IN SCIENCE, THE ANSWER TO EVERY QUESTION provokes another question. Ernest Rutherford, puzzling over the Curie effects, asked, "What is this radiation? And why?"

Rutherford was the son of a Scots emigrant to New Zealand. His father established the first flax mill in South Island. His mother was the first woman schoolteacher in New Zealand. They had twelve children, of whom Ernest was the fourth. He was brought up in a real frontier atmosphere, and it entered into the nature of the man. Life was hard, but it was adventurous. His education was in a state primary school from which children at the age of thirteen could get grants of scholarships to secondary schools and from there to the infant universities. Rutherford had no intention of following an academic career. He was no bookworm. He was good in any rough-and-tumble and a keen football player, but he was good at Latin and he had a mechanical mind and a passion for music. At Nelson College, a state boarding school, he was an outstanding pupil, and because his masters expected it of him, he applied for a scholarship to Canterbury College and won it.

The college in those days was a very humble academic institution, with seven professors and a hundred and fifty students. Its science laboratory—for both physics and chemistry—was a tin shack. But he was lucky with his teachers there. The physics professor was an eccentric (by the academic standards of the day), who appreciated originality more than precision. But he was counterbalanced by the mathematics professor, who was a strict pedant. The one gave Rutherford adventurous versatility of thought; the other gave him his discipline.

Rutherford, as a student of twenty-three, became fascinated by Hertz's work on radio waves, and in the cloakroom of the college, where the students hung their gowns, he found a corner for his own private experiments. He could detect signals at a distance of two miles.

Rutherford won a scholarship which took him to Britain and the Cavendish Laboratory at Cambridge. The Cavendish was known as the String-and-Sealing-Wax Laboratory because there they had to devise and make their own apparatus out of anything that was available. The funds appropriated for the equipment and work for forty postgraduate research students amounted to barely £500 a year—about $1,500, on present-day exchange rates. At Cambridge, Rutherford used the rays from uranium, as he and J. J. Thomson had previously used X rays, to activate gases, and he found that the rays were of two different kinds which he called A and B, but he used the Greek characters, so that they became known as *alpha* and *beta* rays. He decided that the alphas were much heavier than the betas. In fact, the alpha turned out to be seven thousand times heavier than the beta. He also applied a magnet to the rays and found that the alphas were positive and the betas negative.

At the age of twenty-seven, Rutherford was appointed to the

Chair of Physics at McGill University, Montreal, and with him, to Canada, moved the focus of atomic research.

One of the many young scientists who chose to throw in their lot with the young New Zealander was an Oxford physical chemist, Frederick Soddy, just twenty-three years old. His association with Rutherford lasted only two years, but that was long enough to change the whole face of physics.

Soddy himself had already done original researches and, when he teamed up with Rutherford, they investigated *thorium,* which, as Marie Curie had shown, was radioactive. They found that *thorium* changed into a new element, *thorium X,* and in the process gave off what was apparently a gas and at the same time a third type of ray, to which they gave the Greek letter *gamma.* We now know that gamma rays are a particularly fierce form of X ray. With daring, the partners announced that "they had proof of what Marie Curie had suspected, that atoms, the indivisible, were in fact dividing." The atoms were splitting of their own accord, constantly changing and withering away.

* * *

From there the story gradually builds up, step by step, until it reaches its climax in the release of atomic energy. In that story scientists of many nationalities were to make their contributions, but until his death in 1937, Rutherford contributed the thread of that story. He was the point of reference to which the international scientists turned. In retrospect it is uncanny to see how this association worked out. For example, a young German chemist called Otto Hahn arrived in Montreal to work with Rutherford. He had already discovered a substance many thousands times more active than thorium. Rutherford was skeptical, but experiments proved the existence of *radio-thorium,* and in the course of time Hahn added *radio-actinium* to his discoveries.

While Hahn was at McGill, a photographer wanted to take a portrait of Rutherford in his laboratory. The photographer, conscious of the academic proprieties of the time, was appalled to find that Rutherford, a professor, was not wearing white cuffs. To have asked Rutherford to change into a stiff shirt would have produced a major crisis, but Hahn saved the situation by lending his detachable cuffs, which figured prominently in the picture. Rutherford in later years used to point to that picture and say, "That's me—Hahn-cuffed."

Hahn was the man who was to prove his master wrong in one major particular. Rutherford to his dying day argued that in practice the atom would always be a "sink of energy" and not a "reservoir." This, of course, was on the basis of the efforts to split the atom artificially by using such things as the Cockcroft-Walton high-voltage accelerator and the Lawrence cyclotron. These between 1932 and 1937 (when Rutherford died) had made it possible to produce high-energy atomic particles and use them to bombard other atoms, to split them and to release energy. For example, the high-voltage accelerator applying a million volts released energy of sixteen million volts from the individual atoms which it split. That sounds like a pretty good dividend. But only one atom-projectile in ten million hit its target. As Rutherford said to me, "It's like trying to shoot a gnat on a dark night and firing ten million rounds of ammunition on the off-chance of hitting it."

He therefore believed that you would have to put more energy into the atom than you would get out of it. But within two years of his death his old friend and colleague, Otto Hahn, had, with Strassman, at the Kaiser Wilhelm Institute in Berlin, shown that when atoms of *uranium* were treated with neutrons, an event took place in which *barium* was left—showing that the uranium atom split as the result of the intervention of the neutron. This announcement was sensational and its consequences were terrific. It was immediately and correctly interpreted by Lise Meitner, then a refugee from the Nazis, in Copenhagen, as making possible a "chain reaction." This merely means that one event is directly followed by another and that produces a third and so on—a neutron upsets the stability inside the core of the atom, causes it to split and to release other neutrons to upset other atoms, to release more neutrons.

Twenty years before Hahn's discovery Rutherford had shown that by using alpha particles naturally released from radium, he could split the nitrogen atom, expel the hydrogen nucleus (or *proton*) from it and change the nitrogen into oxygen. He had proved what the medieval alchemists had believed, at the price of being broken at the rack or burned at the stake, that substances could be transmuted. He had founded Modern Alchemy.

Perhaps even more important than this eventful experiment was the lecture he gave to The Royal Society in 1920. This was one of the classic pronouncements of all time, because he not only reviewed what was already known about the atom but charted what was to come. It was as though Christopher Columbus, instead of merely believing that by sailing westward across the Atlantic he could reach India, had predicted not only the discovery of the New World but also the individual islands of the Caribbean. One of the things Rutherford predicted in that address was the existence of a particle which would consist of two hydrogen nuclei enclosed by the orbit of one electron. (Professor Harold Urey, the United States Nobel-Prize winner, was to discover heavy hydrogen, which is just that.) Another prediction was the existence of a hydrogen nucleus without an electric charge—a neutral particle that would move freely through matter and even enter into the structure of the nucleus itself. This was remarkable foresight, because he was predicting discoveries which were not made for another ten years.

The *neutron,* this neutral particle, was the first discovered and, although it was established by Professor Chadwick, working with Rutherford at the Cavendish Laboratory, it was historically another link with Marie Curie.

* * *

A poor boy, Frédéric Joliot, from the back streets of Paris, had been a pupil of Professor Langevin, at L'Ecole de Paris. Langevin had been associated with the brothers Curie and had helped with their work on piezo electricity. He had been at the Cavendish Laboratory as a colleague of Rutherford in that eventful year which followed J. J. Thomson's discovery of the electron. Joliot was extremely bright, and Langevin eventually sent him to his friend Madame Curie, to get a humble and poorly paid job as a junior assistant at the Institute of Radium. In 1926 Irène Curie, that child whose fifteenth tooth coincided with the discovery of radium, told her mother that she was going to marry this junior assistant. This was the story of the Curies repeating itself, and it was as momentous a partnership, because while the Curies had discovered *natural radium* and got the Nobel Prize for it, the Joliot-Curies discovered *artificial radium* or, rather, artificial radioactivity, and got the Nobel Prize for it.

Bothe and Becker, two German scientists, had noticed that a light and tough metal, *beryllium,* when bombarded with alpha particles from Marie Curie's polonium, gave off powerful radiations. The Joliot-Curies noticed that this radiation had peculiar characteristics. When it passed through a hydrogen compound, like paraffin wax, it drove out hydrogen nuclei with great force. They also noticed that these particles from beryllium left no track in the detecting devices, which meant that they had no electric charge. Their communication in "Nature" was an obscure one. But Rutherford sensed its significance. He handed it to Chadwick, with the characteristic remark, "There's something in this. You ought to look into it."

Chadwick followed up their work and proved by experimental evidence that these were the neutral particles which Rutherford had foreseen—neutrons.

Another discovery followed quickly. Anderson, at the University of California, detected the existence of a *positron* or positive electron. This was a particle of the same size as the negative electron discovered by J. J. Thomson, but when a magnet was applied, the particles swung to the right instead of to the left.

This was the confirmation for which the Joliot-Curies were looking. They found, in 1933, that by bombarding *aluminum* with alpha particles from polonium, they released *positrons.*

They tried other elements and found, for example, that when *boron* was thus bombarded, it turned into *nitrogen,* but a different kind of nitrogen, because it gave off rays like radium. Enrico Fermi, the Italian, followed up their work and led the production of more and more of these new forms of elements. One of these was *plutonium*—a new manmade element which eventually was to form the charge of the atom bomb which destroyed Nagasaki.

The Joliot-Curies, pursuing their work on artificial radioactivity, exposed uranium, that naturally radioactive substance, to a bombardment of neutrons with curious results. Their experiments were followed up by Hahn and Strassman, who provided the chemical evidence on which the subsequent physical theory of chain reaction was based.

* * *

The story from there onwards is substantially the story of the Manhattan Project. Nuclear fission, on which depends the explosion of the atom bomb or the controlled release of atomic energy for industrial purposes, is governed by the release of neutrons. Uranium metal is made up of what are called uranium 238 and uranium 235, in proportions of 140 to 1. The numbers indicate that these are twin elements or *isotopes;* that is to say, that they are chemically identical, but have a different mass. The uranium 235 when bombarded by neutrons splits and gives off neutrons, so that if you can collect enough uranium 235, you can have each of the atoms helping to split the next—if necessary with the violence of the atom bomb. Or you can put uranium, containing both the isotopes, into what is called an atomic pile or reactor, in which it is contrived that all or most of the foot-loose neutrons are put back to work. Thus the neutrons from uranium 235 enter into the nucleus of uranium 238 and produces neptunium, which quickly changes to plutonium. Plutonium is not detectable in nature, because in nature uranium is not arranged in the conditions which exist in the artificial pile, in which the stray neutrons are shepherded into the atom by graphite or heavy water, two substances which slow down the neutrons.

The ultimate achievement of the release of atomic energy depended as much on the technologists as on the scientists. The scientists from their experiments could work out the theoretical conditions under which uranium 235 could be separated from uranium 238, or by which uranium 238 could be turned into plutonium. But in the upshot it depended on the ability of the engineers, industrial chemists and industrial metallurgists to reproduce on a vast scale the conditions which the scientists had conceived in their laboratories. It was, if you like, the technologists who brought about what Rutherford could not foresee in 1937, the turning of his plaything, the atom, into a bursting dam of energy.

*   *   *

Ernest, Lord Rutherford, who, not only by his work, but by his personality and influence, infected all the leading nuclear physicists of our time, was buried in Westminster Abbey alongside Isaac Newton and near to "rare Ben Jonson." In death, at least, Science and the Arts are not divided.

Great Discoveries (3)

1. THE BIRTH-CRIES OF THE STARS

IN THE YEAR 1931, AN AMERICAN RADIO ENGINEER, the late J. G. Jansky, of the Bell Telephone Laboratories, was studying the behavior of atmospherics which interfere with radio reception. He noted that there was a persistent hiss in his earphones as he turned his aerial in a certain direction. With impressive scientific awareness, he recognized the unexpected. Repeatedly, the same thing happened: if the aerial was pointing toward the Milky Way, the hissing started. And he rightly deduced that the explanation was that there were radio waves coming from the stars themselves and that the hissing from the direction of the Milky Way was caused by the combined effect of so many stars. It was like the distant sound of a ball game, but when he tried to identify the sources more precisely—tried to locate the arena, to discover who was cheering whom and, indeed, spot the cheerleader—he was unsuccessful. Jansky was the Man with the Method, but the Moment had not yet arrived. Nevertheless, he had founded an entirely new science—the science of Radio-Astronomy.

* * *

Today, in the country parish of Barnshaw-cum-Goostrey, in the middle of the green fields and flowering hedgerows of Cheshire, England, the births and deaths of stars are registered. A pencil of green light scribbles a message. It is an announcement signaled by a transmitter a million, million, million miles away in space. The transmitter is the infant, or the dying star itself, and the signals are the birth wails or the death rattles uttered long ago, when life was just beginning to appear on this earth. They have traveled so far that even with the speed of light, 186,000 miles per second, they have taken all that time to traverse space and be picked up by the manmade receivers of the twentieth-century.

The latest receiver, at the Cheshire Radio-Observatory of the University of Manchester, has been designed to sweep the full circle of the horizon and the complete arc of the Northern Hemispheric heavens. For comparison, the world's greatest optical telescope, the Giant Eye of Palomar, has a mirror *two hundred inches* in diameter to collect the light from the distant stars; the radio-reflector, to collect the star signals, is *two hundred and fifty feet* in diameter.

The infant science has already proved its marvels: it can identify stars which are invisible because they have no radiant light; penetrate the mask of star dust which hides great areas of our Milky Way; search space for those ghostly dances in which galaxies merge and mingle; track meteors in broad daylight and observe those space-bullets, the cosmic rays, splitting atoms in our upper atmosphere. No clouds can shroud the mysteries of the heavens from the radio astronomer. No star dust can blind him. The Seven Veils of the Cosmos are drawn aside for him.

Consider this: in 1054 the Chinese witnessed and recorded a celestial catastrophe. A star exploded. This phenomenon, which is called a "supernova," means that a celestial body, similar to our own sun, suddenly "triggers off" and expands in flaming gases to many times its own diameter. The optical astronomers identify this Chinese event with the Crab Nebula, still visible in the heavens as a hot, expanding gaseous envelope, the luminous ghost of a departed sun. Bolton, an Australian radio astronomer, got strong signals from a sector of the sky; he narrowed down the search until he located the "transmitter"; it was in the Crab Nebula and it was giving a broadcast account of the event which the Chinese witnessed all those centuries ago.

In 1572 Tycho Brahe, the astonomer, recorded a supernova. Five hundred years later the most powerful telescope can find no trace of it, even as luminous fragments; but Hanbury Brown, in 1952, at the Manchester University Radio-Observatory, got strong signals coming from a blank space in the heavens. He checked and others rechecked, and they showed that the signals came from Tycho Brahe's supernova. They had been picking up the death rattle of a long-departed star.

The two most powerful celestial transmitters are in the constellations Cassiopeia and Cygnus. They were favorite radio stations for the radio astronomers who listened regularly to the gibberish of their programs. Then the optical astronomers at Mount Palomar joined in; Baade and Minkowski found that the Cygnus phenomenon was caused by a collision of two galaxies. Imagine what that means: a galaxy is a vast collection of stars (not just planets like the Earth, the Moon, or Mars or Venus, but Suns); the Milky Way, one such galaxy, consists of 100,000,000,000 "suns"; and two such galaxies are in collision, not head on, but mingling and interweaving, like the chorus in a Hollywood musical spectacle.

2. THE PEDIGREE OF AN INFANT SCIENCE

RADIO ASTRONOMY IS AN INFANT SCIENCE of great promise. But let us examine its pedigree and its parentage. On one side, of course, there is optical astronomy going back all those thousands of years and evolving through Copernicus, Tycho Brahe, Kepler, Galileo and Newton. On the other side, there is radio.

We can go back more than a century to Faraday and his *Thoughts on Ray Vibrations* and to Joseph Henry's accounts of his experiments with parallel wires stretched across the campus in front of Nassau Hall, at Princeton, and of the signals, without wires, which passed between. We can pass on to Clerk Maxwell, first director of the Cavendish Laboratory, Cambridge, who provided the electromagnetic theory of light, and to Heinrich Hertz's demonstration that radio waves and light waves differ in wave length only. And we might pause and notice that Hertz, experimenting in 1886, proved that radio waves were reflected from solid objects; he noticed, and proved, that they were echoed and reflected first from two pillars in his laboratory and later from a zinc screen—the first example of radar, which became an important factor in the parentage of radio astronomy. Marconi, of course, figures in the pedigree and Sir Oliver Lodge. Lodge, moreover, was another Man-Before-The-Moment, because in 1900 he tried to discover whether he could detect radio waves from the sun, but his wireless receiver, the coherer, was too primitive.

But we also have to bring in atomic physics, because J. J. Thomson's electrons had to be harnessed to the detector and amplifying valves and to the many devices we now call "electronic," without which radio astronomy would be impossible.

Then there was "fundamental applied" research into wave propagation. We can recall how scientists in Marconi's day, on the basis of their own sound reasoning, told him he was mad to think that he could send wireless signals across the Atlantic, since, the world being curved, the signals would fly off into space, at the horizon. When he proved them wrong, they had to provide another theory. Oliver Heaviside, in Britain, and Professor A. E. Kennelly, in the United States, independently and simultaneously, suggested that there was an electric "ceiling" enclosing the earth, which reflected back Marconi's radio waves.

After the First World War, a young Yorkshireman, Edward Appleton, joined Rutherford's team at Cambridge and proposed, as his own program of research, the testing of the nature and height of the Kennelly-Heaviside Layer. He, and his colleague Barnett, proceeded to prove that the Layer varied in distance from the earth, at between sixty and seventy miles up, according to the time of the day. His technique was to check the height of the "electric ceiling" by varying the frequencies of a radio transmitter.

* * *

In 1924, Dr. Gregory Breit and Dr. Merle Tuve, at the Carnegie Institute, reported that by jerking out a short pulse of radio they would get an echo, just like the response of sound waves in echo sounding at sea. The pulse echo was a much simpler device for depth finding than wobbling radio waves.

Appleton had meanwhile found that while some waves were reflected from the Kennelly-Heaviside Layer, others got through and were reflected back by a higher layer, which he showed to be about a hundred and thirty miles above the earth. One can think of the lower layer as a ceiling with slats. Longer wave lengths could not get through the slats and were turned back, but shorter waves escaped and bounced off the ceiling in the upper story, the "F" or "Appleton" Layer. With the help of the Breit-Tuve pulses and a cathode-ray oscillograph (like a television tube, in which signals become luminous squiggles on a screen) he was able to make constant checks on the two layers—an important consideration in the development of world-wide communications. But in the course of his experiments a significant incident occurred.

He was using a transmitter belonging to the Government Post Office, and the post office engineers noticed that there were curious hitches in the transmissions. They noticed, too, that the interference coincided with the flight schedules of aircraft from a near-by airport. The radio waves were being reflected back from the aircraft in flight, just as they were being echoed from the atmospheric layers—and had been echoed by the pillars in Hertz's laboratory. These technicians are completely anonymous, but their shrewd observation was to mean death to the German Luftwaffe.

3. RADAR

THAT BRINGS US TO RADAR. In 1934 the British Air Ministry, aware that Britain was no longer an island and was wide open to bomber attack, set up a committee of scientists to investigate every device which might help in air defense. Nothing was ruled out—not even death rays, long beloved by the cartoon strips. Death rays were referred to the superintendent of the Government Radio Research Department, Robert Watson-Watt, who gave a quick answer. He and a colleague, A. F. Wilkins, reckoned the amount of energy which would be needed to stall an engine. It was far beyond the practical capacity of any transmitter *but*. . . .

This was the *but* which was to decide the fate of a nation. *But,* reported Watson-Watt, the amount of energy needed to *detect,* instead of *destroy,* an enemy aircraft could be reasonably produced and applied by the extension of radio methods. This historic remark was on half a sheet of note paper and was based on calculations which took barely half an hour, and it included Watson-Watt's opinion that location of aircraft by radio was worth pursuing. He was told to go and pursue it.

As a result, within a month he gave a demonstration of how an aircraft could be detected at a distance. That was just a beginning, since while the device detected the presence of an enemy, it did not give his height and bearings. The methods of giving that information had to be worked out, and this demanded shorter wave lengths and more delicate instruments than hitherto employed. But eventually it meant that by the outbreak of war, Britain had a network of detectors which, in the Battle of Britain, were capable of guiding a fighter-interceptor to his target by directions from the ground.

The next thing was to give the pilot his own sixth sense, in the form of a radar apparatus capable of sending out and receiving echoes, as a bat sends out and receives its squeaks. That came about in an unexpected way.

As has been said, the need was for shorter and shorter wave lengths and for an exact way of measuring these wave lengths. The measurement of centimeter-length waves was not easy. The job was given to a team at Birmingham University, which included J. T. Randall, J. Sayers, and H. A. H. Boot. They produced, not a measuring device, but the "cavity magnetron," which remains the "heart of radar."

Perhaps you have blown across the hole, or cavity, of an old-fashioned door key and have had your breath changed into a shrill whistle, or maybe you have been more enterprising and have played the Pipes of Pan, getting different whistles, or sound frequencies, from the different lengths of reed. That, roughly, is the principle of the cavity magnetron, except that the "whistle" is silent and produced by gusts of electrons instead of puffs of breath.

The team took a round chunk of copper, bored out the center, and round the circumference of the inner hole they bored eight smaller holes. They cut slots or passages from the inner hole to the outer ones. Dead center, down the inner hole, they placed a cathode, a negatively charged piece of metal which, when heated, threw off electrons, like the filament of an electric lamp. In an ordinary wireless tube, these electrons shoot off in a straight line, but in this case a magnetic field was applied which made the electrons travel in a circle, round and round the main borehole. This whirlwind of electrons whistled past the slots, thus producing oscillations in the cavities. When one cavity began to oscillate, it induced sympathetic oscillations in its neighbor (just as an oscillating radio set in the next apartment will produce a whistle in yours), and so a crescendo of frequencies was built up in the eight "whistling" cavities.

Since the original instruction had been to measure centimeter wave lengths, the size of each cavity was such that it would produce 3,000,000,000 vibrations a second, which is the frequency of a ten-centimeter wave length in space. Just as a siren works itself into a shrill frenzy and lets out an eldritch shriek, so the swirl of electrons built up a shrill (but inaudible) electric note in each of the eight cavities, and sent out a piercing pulse, then built up another and so on. The inaudible electric "shriek" lasted only a millionth of a second, which is right for radar echoes, and was repeated a thousand times a second. That pulse had an energy of 800 kilowatts, the energy of a powerful radio transmitter.

Instead of a measuring device, they had produced an instrument no bigger than the sound box of an old-fashioned phonograph, but with the power of a radio station.

In *Scientists Against Time,* the official U. S. history of science in war, the cavity magnetron is described as "the most valuable cargo ever brought to our shores." It arrived in America in the baggage of Sir Henry Tizard, who could carry it in his coat pocket.

With a portable transmitter of such power and precision and with centimeter wave lengths to give sharper definition to the radar-screen pictures, not only interception but "blind bombing" became possible. "Blind bombing," which enables the outlines of a target to become visible (on a radar screen) no matter whether it is pitch-dark or whether the target is masked by clouds or by a smoke screen, was a consequence of interception. It was found that when the radar beam was too wide, the rays not only picked out the target but spread to the ground. So they got echoes both from the enemy aircraft and from the ground. That was "cleaned up" by using the new very short wave lengths, but the lesson was not missed. Why not use a radar "searchlight," beamed downwards on a ground target?

This was "H_2S," which is the chemical symbol for sulphureted hydrogen, the odor of rotten eggs. It got that undignified name through Lord Cherwell, then Churchill's scientific adviser. Cherwell, when shown the device, thought that it was so obvious that someone should have thought of it earlier. "It stinks," he said. Hence H_2S.

4. THE ASTRONOMER'S APPRENTICES

WHAT ON EARTH HAS THE cavity magnetron and blind bombing to do with radio astronomy? A great deal. Radar was demanding shorter and shorter wave lengths, and in the wartime discussions which went on about wave lengths, academic arguments returned to Jansky and to the possibility of ultra-short radiations from space.

The transmission of short-wave lengths meant that instruments had to be designed to receive them. So receivers became more and more refined.

As to blind bombing, one of those responsible for H_2S was A. C. B. Lovell (later the first professor of radio astronomy in the world). After the war, he went to Manchester University to join forces with Professor P. M. S. Blackett and to work on cosmic rays.

The new extrasensitive transmitters were available after the war. So was the radar technique. J. S. Hey, an associate of Appleton, started researches into radio emanations from the sun and succeeded where Oliver Lodge, fifty years before, had failed. He turned his detectors on the Milky Way and was able to confirm what Jansky had suspected in 1931—that radio signals were coming from the galaxy and could be identified with particular sources in the star clusters.

Using the radar technique, the U. S. Signal Corps, in January, 1946, shot radar pulses at the moon and got an echo back in less than three seconds, which corresponded to the time it would take to make a radio round trip of 478,000 miles.

The original idea at Manchester University was to use Lovell's experience and the instruments then available, as postwar military surplus, to study cosmic-ray showers. When cosmic rays—high-speed particles from space—hit the earth's atmosphere they smash the atoms of the atmosphere and release a burst of atomic particles. Some of them disappear at great height; some can be trapped (by detectors, like photographic plates or Geiger counters) on the tops of mountains; some can be detected at sea level; and some are powerful enough to penetrate to depths underground. It was considered that radar could locate those bursts in the upper atmosphere just as it had located enemy aircraft. So, in an old fertilizer shed at Jodrell Bank, the University's botanical station in Cheshire, and with trailers and equipment bought and borrowed from the services, the radar gypsies squatted in what looked like a muddy fairground. They got their apparatus working, but their results were complicated by "false' signals which had nothing to do with their echoes from cosmic rays. These signals were perplexing until they found that they were getting radar echoes from meteors. That meant that they could observe meteors, not only at night, but in broad daylight and in all weathers. They found new meteor showers. (Meteors are most likely the debris of comets.) When these particles are caught in the earth's atmosphere, the friction heats them so that they glow in the darkness as shooting stars. But they also leave an ionized track—that is, electrify the gases through which they pass—and it is this track which gives the radar echo. Obviously those tracks will echo even in the daytime when the glow will be invisible. The first bursts of celestial fireworks were noticed on the instruments in the month of August and coincided with the annual return of the Persids, but later on the radar screen they started to spark like a lighter flint—swarms of tracks particularly during the day, and they were coming from the direction from which visual astronomers had no reason to expect them—from the direction of the constellation Pisces. They went on for months and with a frequency more intense than any meteor shower on record. The "Piscids" had been added to the textbooks of astronomy. Thus "blind astronomy" replaced the chasing of cosmic-ray bursts, and the team settled down, not only to await replies to their own signals in the form of radar echoes, but to detect and receive signals initiated by the "transmitters" in space, and to chart the Dark Stars in the heavens and to study the cosmography of the nebulae, those universes including and beyond the Milky Way.

*   *   *

The birth of a new science, which we are witnessing in our own generation, is an admirable example of *The Method, The Man* and *The Moment.* The Method takes no account of the differences of nomenclature between the "pure" and "applied" sciences and technology. A radio engineer, Jansky, trying to unsnarl the practical problem of atmospheric interference, made a series of observations, in which he noticed the consistency of hissing from the direction of the Milky Way. It is immaterial whether he knew anything of Oliver Lodge's inspired guess about the possibility of radio waves from the sun; Jansky set up his own hypothesis—that there were radiating sources in the Milky Way. The fact that he did not have the accurate instruments with which to confirm the hypothesis did not destroy it. A hypothesis does not die when it is unproven; only when it is disproven. Others, in this case, could provide the proof when The Moment was appropriate. It also shows that the development of discoveries is like a relay race in which one runner passes the baton to the next. It shows that at each stage the approach is relatively simple, while the idea is still uncomplicated by language. Radar is now a highly complicated subject, yet it began as half a sheet of note paper. Radio astronomy is full of complicated symbols and calculations, yet it began as "something coming from the Milky Way."

Great Discoveries (4)

1. THE DOG THAT DID NOT BARK

IN SEPTEMBER, 1928, ALEXANDER FLEMING came back from a week's vacation to his laboratory at St. Mary's Hospital, Paddington, London. Before leaving he had started some germ cultures in round, shallow dishes, and he now examined them to see how they had multiplied and whether the colonies of germs had bred true to the original type. Some had been contaminated with other bacteria—an expert glance told him that—and he discarded them. One he picked up from the window ledge. It, too, had been spoiled.

Just as he was about to reject it he paused. The fate of millions of human beings hung upon that instant's hesitation. Instead of casting it aside, he looked again. And he looked hard. There was a patch of mold about the size of a fifty-cent piece. Around it was a clear moat separating the mold from the colony of *staphylococci*. "Interesting!" he said to his roommate. And he proceeded to investigate.

* * *

Usually the clue to a scientific discovery is the observation of something that *is* there. In the case of penicillin, the clue was something that *was not* there.

" 'Is there any other point to which you wish to draw my attention?' asked Dr. Watson (in Conan Doyle's *Silver Blaze*).

" 'To the curious incident of the dog in the night-time.'

" 'The dog did nothing in the night-time.'

" 'That was the curious incident,' remarked Sherlock Holmes."

The dog which did not bark in the case of penicillin was the fact (which Fleming noted) that there were no germs around the mold.

*   *   *

Here is the perfect setting for the popular legend which has grown up around the discovery of penicillin. It has all the whimsy of J. M. Barrie's *Peter Pan.* ("And little Fairy Fluff skipped in through the window and hopped on the plate. And, hey, presto! There was penicillin.") And it is a legend which does less than justice to Sir Alexander Fleming and to the others who gave us penicillin as the life-saving substance we now use.

Fleming never produced penicillin as we know it today. He certainly gave it the name in a scientific report which he prepared in 1929. In this he wrote: "So for convenience and to avoid the repetition of the rather cumbersome phrase 'mold broth filtrate' the name *penicillin* will be used. This will denote the filtrate of a broth culture of the particular *penicillium* with which we are concerned." (*Penicillium* is the name for a group of molds which shoot out brushlike growths.) But Fleming never extracted the active principle from the filtrate; he, through no fault of his own, described the mold as a type of *penicillium* different from what it actually was; and he did not recognize the property which makes penicillin so important—that it can destroy germs *within the living body*.

He noted the *effect* of the mold on his germ colony in September, 1928. He handled the yellow powder, the real penicillin, for the first time fourteen years later, in August, 1942, when Professor Florey of Oxford University gave him all the stock which existed in the world at that date, and Fleming used it to save the life of a friend who was undoubtedly dying of meningitis and who recovered as a result.

The object of this recital is not to "debunk" Sir Alexander Fleming's part in one of the greatest humanitarian discoveries in the history of science, but to illustrate from this supreme example the importance of *The Method, The Man* and *The Moment*.

It is true that no one knows how the spore of *penicillium notatum* (and not *penicillium rubrum,* as Fleming was told it was by the mold expert he consulted) got on that germ plate. It may have drifted in from Paddington Railway Station, above which Fleming's laboratory stood. And that, in itself, might justify it being called a "scientific accident." There is no such thing as a "scientific accident." As in this case, an "accident" is *the impact of an observed fact on a prepared mind.*

Fleming's was certainly a prepared mind. His whole career had been that of a careful, methodical research scientist. His origins were remote from science—a boy from a hill farm in Ayrshire, Scotland. He had come to London to take a job as a shipping clerk and to live with a brother who was a doctor. Like Hopkins, he was enabled to enter the field of science by a small legacy which paid for his education as a doctor. As a student, he fell under the influence, and commanded the respect of Sir Almroth Wright, who was the original of "Sir Colenso Ridgeon" in Shaw's *The Doctor's Dilemma.* Wright had a great reputation as the man who discovered "opsonin," a substance in the blood which enables the white blood corpuscles to resist or devour bacteria and who showed that the body could be encouraged to produce "opsonin" by taking some of the patient's own germs, cultivating them in the laboratory, killing them and then injecting the bacterial corpses into the patient's body. So, when Wright offered his capable student a post as his assistant, Fleming gave up the idea of becoming a physician and, with his medical degree, became a research worker instead.

He was a superb laboratory worker. His techniques were classical examples of modern laboratory practice and his knowledge of germ behavior and of body reactions to them was unsurpassed. His scientific colleagues would accept anything he put forward as a sound and cautious appraisal. When, therefore, his paper *On the Antibacterial Action of Cultures of Penicillin with Special Reference to their Use in the Isolation of B. Influenzae* appeared in 1929, it was accepted as "a nice job of work," no more, no less. And Fleming was putting it no higher than that—a laboratory method by which penicillin killed off germs in a test tube but could not kill Pfeiffer's bacillus.

But there was another reason why Fleming hesitated before he threw away the "spoiled" germ plate. He had to his own credit the discovery of *lysozyme.* This is a natural property, best exemplified by tears, by which germs are dissolved. It explains why that fairly delicate organ, the eye, which is exposed to the multitude of germs which infest the air, is so rarely infected. Fleming would demonstrate *lysozyme* by scraping a cluster of germs off a culture plate, putting them in a test tube with distilled water and shaking it until it was murky. He would then jerk an unemotional tear into his eye, remove it with a fountain-pen filler and drop it into the test tube. Almost immediately the murkiness would disappear; the tear had "liquidated" the germs; and that is "lysis." Tears, he would explain, are very powerful germ killers. Even in weak solutions of tears, sensitive germs die. Other secretions of the body contain this active principle—sweat, saliva, mucus in the nose and throat, and the gastric juices; and Fleming, ten years before he noticed the clear moat round the piece of mold on his germ plate, had identified the particular substance which has this property.

When, therefore, the *observed fact* of that clear ring round the mold impacted on the *prepared mind* of Fleming, he recognized it as "lysis." The mold was exuding something which was preventing the germs from growing in its neighborhood; it might be a form of *lysozyme*. He took spores of the intruder mold and cultivated it until he had ample reserves of the mold. Then he put scores of the mold in a dish covered with agar, the gelatinous substance on which bacteriologists "farm" their germs. Then he streaked across the dish six different kinds of germs—staphylococci, streptococci, and the bacilli of diphtheria, anthrax, typhoid and coli. There was no doubt that there was a pretty powerful secretion from the mold because, while the germs of the last two grew close up to the mold, the other four could not grow to within a considerable distance of it.

So he took the broth in which the mold grew abundantly and filtered it to get what was only a crude extract of the substance. He used it for selective treatment of germs in test tubes and he tried it on certain types of infection in patients, but only those which, like boils, could be treated on the surface. It "worked," but no better than the antiseptic treatments already cheaply available and, anyway, the filtrate lost its properties so quickly that it was almost a waste of time to make it. He admitted later that neither he nor anyone else at that time thought of using penicillin internally, to attack the disease within the patient's body.

And, apart from an unsuccessful attempt by a famous biochemist, as a matter of laboratory curiosity, to purify the mold filtrate, that was how penicillin remained—a curiosity in the literature—until 1939.

2. THE MAGIC BULLET

WHY? THE REASONS ARE IMPORTANT to this discussion because, so far, the impression has been conveyed that science is a regular progression. Indeed, in the last chapter, the simile was used of a relay race in which each runner hands the baton to the next. Here was a case where the baton had been dropped.

Sometimes, when one is following up an interesting development which looks as though it ought to have commercial possibilities, one finds that it suddenly disappears. It has been bought up and suppressed. Only the commercial concerns do not call it that: they say, "It has been put in the icebox." It is something which is "economically inexpedient"—a process which would supplant existing processes, or a new material which would destroy the market for a good-selling line, or a new technique which would render expensive plants obsolete. So it is quietly "withheld" until a more opportune moment.

But there was nothing like that about the circumstances we are considering. What went astray was a scientific fact, well known not only to doctors, to chemists, to bacteriologists, but to the public, and so obvious that its real meaning had been forgotten. It was so well known, indeed, that Hollywood had made a romantic film about it—*The Magic Bullet,* the story of Paul Ehrlich and his discovery of "606" or "Salvarsan." Since 1910 it had been used everywhere as a treatment for syphilis. That was the trouble—people remembered that Ehrlich had discovered a drug but forgot that he had discovered a principle.

Paul Ehrlich (1854-1915) had been, by the exacting academic standards of his German schools and university, an unsatisfactory student. He had a marked disinclination to attend set lectures or to observe the academic rituals; he preferred to potter around the chemical laboratory, fiddling with dyes. Indeed, when the great scientist Koch went to Breslau, the professors hustled him past an untidy corner of the prim barrack room of a laboratory: it was Ehrlich's disreputable bench. When, after failure, he finally qualified in medicine and entered his thesis for his doctorate, the faculty was flabbergasted. The unpredictable Ehrlich had produced a brilliant paper on staining thin sections of body tissue to make them identifiable under the microscope. So the apparently frivolous playing around with coal-tar dyes had not been merely contempt for university conventions.

His method of approach in those early experiments was profoundly to affect the development of both physiology and chemistry. Instead of looking only at the cells of corpses, he showed how chemicals affected the living cells. He studied the symptoms of lead poisoning in rabbits and noticed that the organs most affected by the poison in the living animals also absorbed lead when the animals were dead. This led him to conclude that certain dyes had a liking for certain tissues and that by injecting different dyes it would be possible to study the organic effects of bacterial disease, and also that germs would pick up different dyes. Using this technique, he was able to distinguish between three different types of white blood corpuscles, and later, his fuschin-dye stain for tubercle bacillus was a contribution to the work of Koch, whose assistant he became.

But the importance of his work to the unfolding story of drugs was his discovery that if cells and tissues, in life as in death, had a way of selecting, or attracting, dyes could be commissioned as express messengers to carry special deliveries to any particular part of the body. When, for instance, he injected methylene blue into an animal, he found that only the nerves, and no other tissues or organs, were stained. Perhaps, he argued, it would be possible to fit methylene blue with a chemical knapsack—attach a fraction of a narcotic to the molecule of dye and ensure that it would be duly delivered to the nervous system, to deaden pain. He also argued that it should be possible to inject into the living body dyes which would not only seek out special tissues but particular germs as well.

He succeeded, after trying five hundred different dyes, in finding one which would seek out the *trypanosomes,* the parasites which, passed on by the bite of the tsetse fly, causes disease in animals and man. The result, "Germanin," was an effective drug against sleeping sickness in human beings. Persistently he went on, and after 606 experiments he produced "Salvarsan" (arsphenamine), a coal-tar dye with a load of arsenic. This could seek out and kill the spyrochete of syphilis. By the time he died he had got, after 914 experiments, neosalvarsan. Or, if you insist, sodiumdiaminodihydroxyarsenobenzenemethanalsulfoxylate.

The experiments, like the name, might be long, but the principle was brief: a drug could *kill a selected germ within the living body,* instead of drugs or inoculations being used to moderate symptoms and give nature a hit-or-miss chance to enable the body to muster its own defenses.

3. THE SULFA DRUGS

DOCTORS WENT ON USING Ehrlich's legacies but forgot his testament. That was how it was in 1928, when Fleming observed the effect of the substance exuded from the growing mold—all right on the germ dish; all right to kill germs in the test tube; and all right to apply to a boil; but not to inject or to swallow. And that was how it was until 1933, when Dr. Gerhard Domagk, working in the Ehrlich tradition, produced "Prontosil."

And this is the story of it: In 1908, seven years before Erhlich's death, a young Austrian, Paul Gelmo, submitted a thesis for his doctorate at the Vienna Institute of Technology. He had synthesized a new coal-tar derivative which he called "para-amino-benzenesulfanomide." Gelmo is important because his was the key sulfanomide which prevented I. G. Farben, the German chemical combine, from succeeding in getting a blocking patent on the subsequent developments. Gelmo is just a shadow cast across history. When Waldemar Kaempfert wrote in the New York *Times* (about 1946) that Gelmo had vanished from human ken, a Viennese science-writer discovered him working as the aged head chemist of an Austrian printing firm, even then unaware that he had unwittingly made a momentous discovery.

Dr. H. Hoerlein, director of the I. G. Farben laboratories, rescued Gelmo's thesis from obscurity. He found it in the literature and recognized that the synthetic would make a good textile dye. The result was a brick-red dye, fast for wool. But it came into the hands of Domagk, the bacteriologist, who, like Ehrlich, was systematically working through an endless series of dyes to find an effective germicide. In 1932, he produced a red dye which "packed a punch." It was patented but attracted little attention. Domagk confined his attentions to laboratory mice until there was an exciting human denouement.

His own young daughter pricked herself with a knitting needle and contracted generalized blood poisoning. The doctors and surgeons did their best but it was not good enough. The girl would surely die. The desperate father decided to risk his own drug—a large dose. She recovered completely. Yet her father was too good a scientist to base any claims on the strength of one case—even though he could vouch for it heart and soul. When, in February, 1935, Domagk presented his experimental evidence for the germicidal properties of "Prontosil" he mentioned only the statistical evidence of his satisfactory mice experiments.

Then, in 1936, the "Miracle Drug" hit the headlines. A serious outbreak of child-bed fever had occurred in Queen Charlotte's Hospital, London. Thirty-eight mothers were in a critical condition. They tried "Prontosil" and only three out of the thirty-eight died. Further results were even more satisfactory. There was no doubt that "Prontosil" was a specific and effective drug for puerperal sepsis, or child-bed fever.

"Prontosil" was a patented product. When the scientists at the Pasteur Institute, in Paris, wanted to find out what was the basis of it, the Germans demurred. But the Frenchmen got hold of the patent specifications and manufactured it themselves, but only to take it to pieces again to discover its secret. They did and they found it was sulfanilamide—a factor which two Americans, Dr. W. A. Jacobs and Dr. Maurice Heidelberger, at the Rockefeller Institute had just missed, as long before as 1919, when they were trying to find a dye "hook-up" for quinine as a possible cure for pneumonia.

Because of Gelmo, the Germans could not sustain their patent, and chemists all over the world got busy producing "sulfas" for many different germ conditions. Ehrlich rode again!

4. THE DISCOVERERS OF PENICILLIN

THE WHOLE "CLIMATE" OF MEDICAL OPINION was changed and that is why, when Fleming's forgotten paper on penicillin was looked at again, it conveyed something quite different. Could this substance, whatever it was, operate internally?

That was just how it struck Ernest Chain when he discovered Fleming's scientific account in the Radcliffe Library at Oxford. Chain had escaped to Britain from Hitler's Germany. He was a brilliant biochemist who became assistant to Howard Florey, an Australian, the professor of pathology at Oxford University.

And here is where the curious weft and woof of science draws another thread across. Florey was interested in lysozyme, Fleming's original discovery. He had made a study of it and had produced it in a pure state, from which it was crystallized. But he was concerned to find out whether there were other possible agents which could similarly dissolve germs, and he gave Chain the assignment.

It was pure coincidence that Fleming's lysozyme should lead Chain to Fleming's penicillin. Until he turned up the paper in the library, he had never heard of penicillin. And at first his curiosity was entirely academic. For one thing, he noticed the kind of germs against which Fleming had shown its laboratory effectiveness. For another, the very quality which had discouraged Fleming as a bacteriologist intrigued Chain as a biochemist—the fact that it lost its potency so quickly.

Anyway, he went off to see whether there was any of the mold in the university. There he had remarkable luck—and here "luck," which is a word scientists do not like, is justified—because they had "The Fleming Mold," a type-culture from the original speck of fungus of eleven years before. So, with the full support of his professor, Chain set to work with the help of other able chemists and, as the work progressed, the significance of the substance became apparent. Because of the awareness created by the sulfa drugs, they regarded it as a possible means of attacking germs *inside the living body.*

Laboriously, they grew the molds, some in milk bottles, and some in bedpans (recall that this was Britain under blitz and short of all equipment). Their apparatus included a Civil Defence stirrup-pump (used for putting out bomb fires), a dog bath, some milk churns and a milk cooler borrowed from a dairy. By such methods, but with all the refinements of the laboratory bench as well, they finally obtained a speck of true penicillin. With this they had to make their microanaylsis and their biological tests and, as painfully, they accumulated enough to enable Professor Florey and his wife to make their first clinical test. A policeman was dying in the local hospital. They used the drug. He rallied and went on improving. The small supply of the drug gave out and he died.

There was, however, no doubt that this was an exceptional drug. Britain could not produce it because its manufacturing resources were fully engaged and there were certainly no engineering facilities to produce new equipment.

Professor Florey and Dr. N. G. Heatley, a chemist whose ingenuity had helped to produce the laboratory supplies, went to the United States in 1941. They went to the Northern Regional Research Laboratory of the U. S. Department of Agriculture, at Peoria, Illinois. Dr. R. D. Coghill, head of the Fermentation Division, lent his assistance. Hitherto the molds had been grown in shallow vessels. It was suggested at Peoria that deep culture in large vats should be used and that corn-steep liquor, a sweet, rich waste product of distilling, should be used as the "food" for the molds. Thus the technological side, the chemical engineering in which America excels, was developed. The patents for the mass-production techniques were American.

The Nobel Prize was awarded jointly to Sir Alexander Fleming, Professor Ernest Chain and Sir Howard Florey—a recognition of the scientific combination of the man who observed the effect, the man who discovered its significance and the man who directed the researches and proved its biological importance.

5. AMERICAN ANTIBIOTICS

AMERICAN SCIENTISTS were quick to follow through. Dr. Selman Waksman made his discovery of streptomycin, for which he was awarded the Nobel Prize. He was an expert on soil organisms at Rutgers University, New Brunswick. He must have examined millions of soil cultures in his time. In 1939, he was studying the relation of soil organisms to disease and in 1940, while the Oxford team was working on penicillin, he produced his first antibiotic—

actinomycin—but it was too poisonous for clinical use. Then with the inexhaustible patience of the trained researcher he examined ten thousand cultures. Only one thousand were found to kill bacteria in laboratory tests. Only a hundred survived the follow-up tests. Only ten were interesting enough to be isolated and fully described and, after four years, only one—streptomycin—survived the search and research.

It was immediately recognized as of major importance because it was observed in laboratory tests to destroy some of the sixty-four germs which had proved intractable to penicillin. Notably it destroyed—in test tubes—the tubercle bacillus. It was almost too much to hope that this was the final answer to the White Plague. Not entirely, but it has by long patient clinical trials proved effective in certain tuberculous conditions and in a whole variety of diseases —including bubonic plague, which decimated the population of Europe in the days of the Black Death and the population of London in the Great Plague.

Other antibiotics, as these new drugs are called, have followed. Of the Big Five—Penicillin, streptomycin, aureomycin, terramycin and chloromycetin—four are American discoveries. U. S. scientists have also produced better strains of *penicillium* molds giving greater yields and more consistent behavior. In 1952, ten years after Fleming saved his friend's life with the whole of Florey's available supply, the United States produced penicillin and other antibiotics to the tune of $644,000,000.

Scientifically, an immense amount is now known about these substances. Penicillium molds have been "bashed about" by X rays, bombarded by atomic particles and treated with colchicine, the chemical of the autumn crocus, to change their hereditary nature, and new strains have been produced artificially. Chemists, almost as soon as it was discovered, set to work to "take it to pieces" and see why it worked. They were beaten to it by a woman, Dorothy Crowfoot Hodgkin, at Oxford. She was a crystallographer—a scientist who, by X rays, examines the nature of crystals—and, by X rays, she found how the atoms were arranged in the molecule of penicillin. Chemists could now, if they wanted to, ignore the mold altogether and build up the penicillin, artificially, but in this case molds are cheaper than Ph.D.'s and do the work most efficiently.

In the case of chloromycetin, this was not so. This was originally found in a sample of mold sent from Venezuela to a botanist at Yale, and it had its first spectacular successes in curing scrub typhus and also typhoid in the jungles of Malaya. Dr. Mildred Rebstock, a twenty-eight-year-old research chemist in Detroit, first produced the synthetic form of the drug and found that it basically contained two chemicals normally poisonous—one was a nitrobenzene compound and the other an acid which is sometimes used to get rid of warts—but in combination they formed this lifesaver. Thus chloromycetin was the first antibiotic to be manufactured synthetically.

The search goes on constantly. It is not a rash prediction to say that presently we will have a complete armory of drugs against the infectious and communicable diseases, although the virus diseases are—for the moment—still intransigent.

Great Discoveries (5)

1. HERE BE DRAGONS

IN FEBRUARY, 1949, THE *WAC-Corporal* took off from White Sands, New Mexico, and reached a height of 250 miles above the earth. For the first twenty miles of the ascent, it was carried by a German V-2 rocket, like those which had been used to bombard Britain in the late stages of the Second World War. When it was released from its carrier, it continued its independent journey at the V-2's speed of over 3,000 miles an hour. The *WAC-Corporal* carried no human freight.

In 1952, William Bridgeman, in the U. S. Navy's D-558-11, the *Skyrocket,* reached a speed of 1,238 miles an hour, and, on another occasion, reached the height of 79,494 feet, beating the record of 72,394 feet made in a balloon by Orville Anderson and Albert Stevens, in 1935. The *Skyrocket* was built for research and for spurts of speed and not for prolonged flight.

These two events are of immense historic importance because they date a new Declaration of Independence, in which Man has declared his determination to free himself from the domination of Mother Earth and to defy, or at least to exploit, the natural "laws" which appeared to set limits to speed and distance. Why he should seek to escape, say, to the moon, when there is so much scope for his ingenuity in dealing with unsolved problems nearer home, is another matter.

H. G. Wells probably answered that best in his film *Things To Come* (dramatized from his book *Shape of Things to Come*). In his film script, as the grand climax, he fired a young couple by space gun to the moon. As the fathers watched the ascent in the mirror of the giant telescope, one of them said:

> "For Man there can be no rest and no ending. He must go on, conquest beyond conquest. This little planet, its winds and ways and all the laws of mind and matter that restrain him. Then the planets about him and at last out across immensity to the stars. And when he has conquered all the deeps of space and all the mysteries of time—still he will be but beginning."

That space journey was Wells's symbolism of the never-ending quest by Man but, like so many of his uncanny prophecies which have been overtaken by events, it is nearer fulfillment than even he would have dared to imagine. It is no longer a question of "maybe" but "when?" The Moon-Columbus has no doubt already been born. Explorers, like William Bridgeman, are already probing their way into The Unknown.

* * *

When the ancient map makers came to the limits of their known world and were aware only of the mysteries of the unexplored, they wrote on their maps, "Here be dragons." On the frontiers of scientific knowledge there are the dragons and demons and Abominable Snowmen of the unexplained.

Theory and laboratory experiments can go so far, and then the issue has to be put to the proof of human courage and endurance. And men die finding out: Scott, of the Antarctic, died on the Edge of the World and John Derry, the British test pilot, died on the Frontiers of Sound. Over a century ago, Sir John Franklin and the crews of the *Erebus* and the *Terror* perished because navigators were convinced that there was a Northwest Passage, linking the Atlantic and the Pacific—and they were right. Today, in aviation, the equivalent of the Northwest Passage is the Sound Barrier. Beyond lies the zone of fantastic speeds of travel which make nonsense of our watches, so that we could have breakfast in New York, after having had lunch the same day in London.

The Sound Barrier lies somewhere between Mach 0.9 and Mach 1.5 (the exact position depends on the shape of the airplane). These may be unfamiliar terms to grownups, but they are in the vocabulary of small boys and are as conventional to engineers and to pilots as latitude and longitude are to navigators.

The Mach numbers explain "subsonic," "trans-sonic" and "supersonic." Roughly, subsonic means anything less than 600 miles an hour; trans-sonic applies to speeds between 600 and 900 miles an hour and supersonic to any speed above that. But only "roughly," because the speed of sound varies according to height. At sea level the speed of sound is 761 miles an hour, and between 40,000 and 100,000 feet it is only 663 miles an hour because of the low temperature. The Austrian scientist, Ernst Mach, suggested that the speed of sound should be taken as a standard 761 miles an hour at ordinary temperatures. Thus Mach number 0.5 means 380 miles per hour (subsonic); Mach 0.9 means 684 miles per hour (trans-sonic) and Mach 1.5 1,140 miles per hour (supersonic).

Man, through the ages, has devised ways of increasing speeds and, in the last hundred and fifty years, has produced more and more efficient engines—steam, internal combustion, jet and rocket propulsion—to give them more and more speed. Surely, then, increasing speed from 380 miles an hour to 1,140 miles an hour is merely a matter of making an engine capable of producing that speed? But, no. Nature is not surrendering as simply as that. The Sound Barrier is not just an abstract idea. It is a physical reality.

This is why: a moving body sends out sound waves in the direction in which it is traveling. If you throw a ball, the ball creates advance waves to blaze the trail—giving the air ahead notice to arrange itself in the proper flow pattern.

These waves are like the motorcycle escort of a procession, or rather like the outriders who go ahead of the procession. At their behest the atmosphere divides, like the crowds getting on the sidewalks and providing a passage for the official cars that follow. At subsonic speeds the outriders are well ahead and the crowds quietly arrange themselves in an orderly way. But if the speed of the processional cars is almost as fast as that of the advance guard, the crowds barely have time to get out of the way, and then only in turbulent confusion. But if the cars are traveling as fast or faster than the motorcyclists who are supposed to be clearing the way, then the crowds have no advance warning. Instead of dividing, they can only jam tighter in a panicking mass with which the procession collides, with disastrous results.

So with sound waves. Suppose an aircraft is traveling at two hundred miles an hour, a thousand feet above the ground. The advance wave it sends out travels at 761 miles an hour and so is moving 561 miles ahead to give ample warning and make an orderly passage—a funnel through the atmosphere. But when, in the trans-sonic speed levels, the aircraft is catching up with its sound waves, the air is thrown into confusion. It no longer flows evenly over the shape of the aircraft. It stumbles and tries to get out of the way. It clutches at the machine, pulls and drags, burbles and swirls, wrenching the structure of the machine and wrestling with the pilot for the possession of the controls. This is the region of the Demons who beset the Sound Barrier; this is the shock wave which has torn machines to pieces and hurled men to their deaths. Then, at the speed of sound, the waves are compressed into a formidable physical obstacle, an invisible wall, which involves a headon collision.

2. BEYOND THE SOUND BARRIER

BEYOND THAT BARRIER, THE AIRCRAFT, traveling faster than the speed of sound, has ripped through and has escaped from its own sound waves. It is ahead of them so that they cannot encumber it. And Sound Barrier pilots will tell you crossing the Barrier is like riding over a fierce surf of the shoals and finding a still lagoon behind. The sensation is that of "riding easy," with no rough handling of the aircraft and no dragging of the controls.

Supersonic speeds, like Bridgeman's *Skyrocket* effort, are usually attained in powered dives—that is, pushing down the nose of a high-speed trans-sonic aircraft and diving earthwards harnessing the power of the engine to the force of gravity. To obtain consistent supersonic speeds in level flight and to produce supersonic airliners means not only increasing the power of the engines but drastic alterations in the design of the aircraft. For example, the swept-back wing and delta-triangle shapes are suitable for transsonic flight but not for supersonic. The arrowhead, or triangle, gives the cutting edge—the ploughshare—which reduces the impact of the shock wave. But at best, the swept-back wing is suitable only up to Mach 1.3—about 900 miles an hour—and beyond that, thin, narrow, straight-wings give the necessary advantages. Engineers and designers, therefore, have to find a combination of the two—an aircraft which will take off and land as a straight-wing, sweep the wings back when approaching the barrier, and straighten them again in the lagoon. Or the answer may be a "Flying Saucer" type.

The metallurgists, too, have their headaches because at supersonic speeds the whole aircraft gets heated to high temperatures. This is not only a question of refrigerating the pilot to keep him from broiling, but of the metals of which the aircraft is constructed. There is the point where, like Icarus who flew too near the sun, the metals might melt like the wax of his wings. The engineers are asking for new metals like titanium or for plastics which will give the necessary resistance to heat.

* * *

There is one problem which is entirely beyond the engineers and for which the scientists cannot yet suggest a practical answer. That is the supersonic bangs which occur when the aircraft crosses or recrosses the Sound Barrier. In power diving, there is a sort of double report, one when the aircraft reaches supersonic speed and again when the speed is reduced. It is like someone charging through a lobby and banging the doors at both ends. The banging can sound like a violent explosion. It is disturbing enough when it is from a diving aircraft, because the sound waves are like a searchlight beam directed at a limited area below. But in level flight the bangs are not so localized. The report of the shock waves spreads outwards like the bow wave of a ship and like that bow wave reaching the shore, so the bang wave reaches the ground along, and around, the line of flight. How violently it will hit the ground will depend on the height of the aircraft.

The prospect before us earthlings in the days of large-scale supersonic flying is of our lives being made hideous by the ripping of the heavens. The engineers cannot provide the answer because the sound (unlike jet noises) has nothing to do with the engine; it is caused entirely by the impact of the aircraft on the atmosphere. Flying at supersonic speeds may have to be restricted to ocean crossings or to altitudes so high that the bangs will be spent before they reach the ground.

* * *

Aviation designers and engineers will boast that their successful assault on the Sound Barrier has proved the scientists wrong. Which is only another way of saying that scientists are human. It is certainly true that if, twenty years ago, you had asked (as I did) a physicist or an aeronautical scientist whether men, in machines, would every fly beyond the speed of sound, he would have said "No." That was not because he was just guessing wrong but because he knew all the facts. They were known before there were airplanes, because bullets and military projectiles had been studied at speeds which may never, indeed, be attained by man-carrying vehicles. They knew all about those shock waves and in later years were able to *see* them by using high-speed cameras to photograph bullets in flight. They knew all about the ideal shapes of wing sections. In the wind tunnels, they had measured the behavior in the subsonic regions and, latterly, in the trans-sonic and supersonic. They knew about the heat generated and they knew about "g," which will be discussed later.

When, for instance, H. G. Wells consulted eminent aerodynamic authorities about the shape of the futuristic aircraft for the film *Things to Come,* he was told that wind-tunnel results showed that the swept-back triangle shape was the ideal, "but of course it was impractical," and he was told not to use it. Being Wells, he did. That was 1934. The Germans Busemann and Betz were already thinking about supersonic planes, and the wartime German Messerschmitt 163, though neither trans-sonic nor supersonic, had swept-back wings. But the scientists who gave the advice to Wells were only human; they thought of the then current conventions of aircraft design and how long it would take to change them. And when they said that supersonic flight was impossible, that was not the verdict of science, but of men thinking of human and technical difficulties. For one thing, they thought that the human body would not be able to stand the strain of acceleration.

3. HUMAN ENDURANCE

WE STILL DO NOT KNOW how much speed-punishment the human body will take, but we know it is a great deal more than would have been expected twenty years ago.

Weights increase with acceleration. The unit is expressed as "g" which is the measure of the force by which gravitation attracts a body to the earth. Normally, we endure 1 g, but if we are accelerated at such a rate that we are subjected to a force four times that of gravity (4 g), our bodies will weigh four times as much. Pilots in power dives have blacked out at 4 g, but with no lasting effect. It has been shown experimentally that even when sitting upright, so that the blood would be drawn away from the upper parts of the body, men can stand 7.5 g without serious discomfort or disability. In a prone position it is possible to endure 10 to 12 g for about three minutes. Accelerations to 17 g—when a 150-pound man would weigh 2,550 pounds—have been applied to human beings and they have survived.

Extensive experiments on the limits of human tolerance have been carried out in the Space Medicine Department at Randolph Field. There volunteers are strapped onto a spinning machine which, by centrifugal force, reproduces the "g" conditions likely to be encountered in a rocket take-off. The volunteers are spun around until they are unconscious, their sensations and their diminishing degree of consciousness being recorded, and they are then unstrapped and tested to see how flesh and blood has stood up to this abnormal treatment. Animals have been sent up in rockets and their reactions studied by remote control and by motion picture records which showed no ill effects when "g" was greater than normal.

4. INTO SPACE

ALL THIS KIND OF THING is preparing, in advance, for the hazardous risks which men will take to escape from the binding forces of this planet.

A London newspaper has already confidently offered its readers places on the first rocket to the moon, and it is quite within the bounds of possibility that in the lifetime of the reader of this book he (or she) will see a manmade moon in the sky. For, whether, in the same time, someone makes a return (or a one-way) trip to the moon or not, and whether the astronauts will fulfill the promise of the "comics" and go wandering in space, there are certain things which are foreseeable in the not too distant future. One is the artificial satellite.

The *WAC-Corporal* came back to earth, but it had reached a height of 250 miles, where the air is so thin that it presents no resistance. If the *WAC-Corporal* had had sufficient speed and had had some steering mechanism to tilt it into a prescribed orbit, it might have circled the earth for centuries after its motors cut out. But its speed, plus that acquired from the V-2, which took it up twenty miles, was only about 5,400 miles an hour, not nearly high enough.

The first artificial moon will need to enter its orbit at a speed of 18,600 miles an hour, or five miles a second. Such a speed, in balance with the forces of gravity, would keep it there, and at the same speed, indefinitely. (Compare the moon: the earth is pulling it towards itself, but a speed of two-thirds of a mile a second, at a range of 238,840 miles, is enough to keep it in its orbit.) A manmade satellite can be placed in any convenient orbit and maintained there, given the appropriate speed. For example, at 350 miles an hour the orbital speed would have to be 4.5 miles a second; at 1,075 miles, 4.4 miles a second; at 4,000 miles, 3.7 miles a second. All such particulars, thanks to Sir Isaac Newton three hundred years ago, can be worked out.

The first satellite would be a watchtower in the sky. It would be equipped with instruments which would collect the masses of information which will be needed before manned space stations could be attempted. The information would be radioed back to earth, telling us the things about which we are not quite sure, that happen in the regions beyond our atmosphere. Those include the possible effects on any man-built structure of intense ultraviolet light, the intensity of cosmic particles and the impingement of meteors, which would be hitting a structure uncushioned by the earth's atmosphere. That may be one of the greatest hazards, for if a grain of sand, hitting the earth's atmosphere, can have force enough to create friction and become luminous as a shooting star, consider the impact of that bullet on the metal skin of a spaceship. There would be plenty to be learned, knowledge which we now acquire either from rockets which have only a few minutes to collect it before they crash back to earth, or from balloons.

There are many questions to be answered before we embark on anything as ambitious as the 200-foot circular space station proposed by Dr. Wernher von Braun. This would be inhabited and would be not only an observatory but an assembly point for construction and servicing rockets for space travel. Given 4 billion dollars and the time, this is probably a practical suggestion.

Anyway, rocket ships and space stations are no longer in the realm of fantasy. They deserve and get serious consideration by scientists who might, only a few years ago, have regarded them as poppycock. They are prepared to discuss quite soberly what happens when a man from a rocket steps out into space, foot-loose and fancy-free, with no gravitational force to give him a sense of balance or of weight; and even how he could drink out of a cup in which the water was as levitational as himself. What would be the biological effects upon him of heavy bombardment of cosmic rays or exposure to ultraviolet light unfiltered by our atmosphere? All kinds of interesting problems are raised, about which scientific laws permit serious speculation.

The scientists, like the rest of us, are aware that in terms of space travel they are standing on the threshold of new developments, with new challenges to science in all its branches—physics, chemistry, metallurgy, biology, physiology, psychology—and being beckoned across new frontiers into the terrain of "Here be dragons."

21682

PART

4

Science
and
Survival

*. . . The future belongs to those who shall have done
most for suffering humanity.*

LOUIS PASTEUR

Science and Survival

1. CAIN AND ABEL

THE BIBLICAL STORY OF CAIN AND ABEL might be read as a powerful allegory of the impact of science on a simple order of society. Abel was the shepherd. He drove his flocks and herds over the scattered pastures of the Middle East. Cain was the New Man, the cultivator, who applied knowledge to the problems of livelihood. The herdsman could get enough forage for his animals during the seasons of the rains, which brought up the herbage of the desert and steppe, but in the dry seasons he had to retreat to the river lands. But the time came when Cain had occupied these river lands and was cultivating his plants, domesticating his animals and nurturing his soil. He had displaced Abel. He had "killed" the nomad.

*　　*　　*

Agriculture, however primitive, or however remote in tradition, is in fact the application of science to the problems of living in settled communities. It is not just the use of artificial fertilizers or selective weed killers, or soil conditioning, or the lavish contribution of science to modern, intensive agriculture.

Long before the nineteenth century and the discovery that plants had sex, and before Mendel and his insight into the hereditary factors of plant breeding, Man had successfully bred, and cross-bred, plants for food or flowers for his esthetic satisfaction. He had domesticated his animals most successfully long before Darwin had given him his authority in the theory of evolution.

Flint sickles found at Mount Carmel suggest that cereals were eaten by the Mesolithic cave dwellers probably before 6000 B.C. The first step in agriculture was to get annual crops on prepared ground within a settlement. In the Mediterranean area, two wheats, wild Einkorn and wild Emmer, together with wild barley, were bred for harvesting. Rye and oats, which came much later, began their career as weeds of the wheat and barley fields. It might be said that the civilizations of Western Asia and Europe depended on wheat and barley and that the extension northward into colder latitudes depended on rye and oats.

The domestication of animals for securing food began about the same time. The first domestic animal was probably the dog, which always seems to have had a natural affinity for Man and was his earliest ally in hunting. Cattle, sheep, goats and pigs were brought in early. The use of the horse, ass, ox and camel for transport and haulage came later. Wool, woven into textiles, in place of pelts, originated probably in 4000 B.C. Dairy farming seems to have begun in Mesopotamia about a thousand years later.

Maize and potato agriculture of Central and South America does not seem to have been derived in any way from the evolution of agriculture in the Middle East, and the millet-and-pig economy of China also seems to have been a separate development.

Agriculture was the basis of that civilization which has been called "The Culture of Cities." Settled cultivation could sustain groups twenty times as large as those of the tribal nomad. The means to harvest and conserve food, instead of having to wander in search of it, meant that within settled communities there were opportunities for specialization of labor, beginning with the weaver and the potter and the flint polisher. Out of that grew our complex trades and crafts which depended on the acquisition of farming skill to produce a surplus of food from the soil and not merely a subsistence for those who worked on it.

2. HOW MANY PEOPLE ON THE LAND?

THIS HISTORICAL APPRECIATION of the development of agriculture is important, because the whole progress of our modern technological civilization depends even more nowadays on this surplus of production from the land, upon how many people of our vast and complicated society, of industrial workers, of services, and of professional "hangers-on" can be maintained by the relatively few on the land.

The American farmer of two hundred years ago was self-sufficient: on his farm he could support himself, his wife, perhaps a few pensioners, a hired man and five or six children. The timber from his land provided his house and his fuel. All his dependents were fed and clothed from his farm. It provided his subsistence. What he had to buy was a minimum—a few tools and a few home amenities. Today, from a similar farm, twenty-five people can be supported—that is, counting heads. But, of course, it is not as clear-cut as that.

If he wants, as he does, the cash from the products of his land, to buy an automobile, he has to contribute to the livelihood of a great many people, as remote from his farm as the oil driller in Saudi Arabia, the rubber tapper in Liberia, and the civil servant in Washington.

And we have to remember that eighty per cent of the people in the world are still peasants. In countries such as India, the problem is how to get the people off the land.

Let us assume that the American farmer of two hundred years ago was working a hundred acres and was maintaining his dependents from that. Let us transfer that hundred acres to India. There, today, it would be maintaining two hundred people. The ancestral land of two hundred years ago would be cut up among the descendants. It would be cultivated by methods much more primitive than the American methods of two hundred years ago. It would be impossible, with all these people on the land, to introduce modern methods, even of the most simple kind. The only answer is to get the people off the land, preferably into rural industries, where the hands would still be locally available at the sowing and the harvesting—that is, until in time those hands would be displaced by machinery.

Says Professor Dudley Stamp, in *Our Under-Developed World:*

In India, agricultural production remains at a relatively inefficient level, because of the vicious circle in which the cultivator is entoiled. He is poor; therefore he cannot buy efficient implements or fertilizers; he plants his seeds laboriously by hand on land which he has scratched with his ox plough. He himself, his family and his animals are undernourished, lacking energy for hard work. Because he cannot afford to buy fuel for cooking, he burns the dung of his cattle, the only available material, thereby robbing the land even of animal manure. Consequently, his crop yields are low; he needs nearly all his produce to feed his family and his few, poor animals, and he has no surplus for sale. Because he has no surplus, he remains poor, and his poverty is increased by his usual indebtedness to the moneylender and by the incidence of such heavy expenses as providing marriage dowries for his daughters.

3. PEANUTS

THE CHALLENGE OF OUR DAY AND AGE is so to bring science and technology into agriculture as to compensate for the science and technology of our city civilization. And yet to remember that agriculture is not just an industry but a Way of Life, in which experience is as valuable as experiment and in which the communion, or conflict, with Nature is at its closest and sharpest. The danger is always in short cuts. It is possible to find a scientific answer to one problem only to create a newer and different one. Purely technological answers are never sufficient, and often perilous, when they dodge the issue of the natural environment.

One of the classic examples was the failure at a cost of nearly $90 million of the British Groundnuts scheme in East Africa. There was a world shortage of vegetable oils, as a result of the war and postwar conditions. What brought it to its height was the threat of famine in India, partly because it was not possible to import rice from Siam or from Burma. The Indian Government, with its new-found independence and with its own people as its first charge, diverted land which had hitherto produced groundnuts (peanuts) for British consumption in the form of vegetable oils, converted into margarine. To meet this shortage the British Government decided, on the scale of a military operation, and with mechanical resources beloved by military operators, to open up a vast tract of Tanganyika. The soil (superficially) was the red soil suitable for peanuts. The climate (superficially) seemed suitable. The only problem (superficially) was to clear the land and get rid of the scrub and plant and harvest peanuts. For this purpose army tanks were converted. Heavy machinery was designed to pull down trees and tear up this scrub; and, in the process, to get rid of the tsetse fly, the carrier of infection and death for animals and men. With difficulty, and with disappointments, this mechanical job proceeded. But Nature rebelled. The soil changed its character. The rainfall and the underground water supplies were not as consistent as at first sight they had appeared. The changing of the vegetation altered the supplies to the springs. The exposed soil took on different characteristics. They had got rid of the tsetse fly but they had got rid also of the bees. Unless they were going to have continuous monoculture of peanuts, which would have desiccated the soil, they had to have alternative crops, and these crops could not be pollinized without the bees. The scheme had to be drastically curtailed and the British tax-payer yelped. What was missing in the great array of specialists and short-cut experts was the naturalist, the ecologist, who understands the balance of nature, who realizes that underground water has a great deal to do with surface vegetation, and that all insects are not malevolent, and that many are indispensable partners with men in the production of food.

4. THE LOST CIVILIZATIONS

THIS WAS MAN'S INTERVENTION on the grand scale—a frontal assault on Nature. But Man has been practicing a war of attrition throughout the whole of his history. He had been outraging Nature, through ignorance, or through quite deliberate and callous exploitation, until Nature rebelled, and its revenge was to rob Man of his means of sustenance. That is the story of the Lost Civilizations.

On behalf of the Natural Sciences Division of UNESCO (United Nations Educational, Scientific and Cultural Organization), I carried out a survey of the deserts of North Africa and the Middle East—the great classical deserts—where fifteen civilizations, empires or cultures, flourished and perished in their own dust. There was no question that from the Western Sahara, through Tunisia, Libya, Egypt, the Sinai Desert, Mesopotamia and the deserts of Persia, the greater part of the desolation was manmade. And here had been the great granaries of Greece, of Rome, of the Pharaohs and of the fabulous civilizations of Babylon and Sumeria. In the

Persian Desert, Nishapur, the birthplace of Omar Khayyám, in his day (eleventh century), or certainly a century later at the time of Genghis Khan, was a great oasis with a population of a million and a half. Today it sustains only 15,000 people. In what is now desert between Kerman and Baluchistan, Alexander the Great sustained an army for two months in a forage-yielding area, where today there is not a single village or hamlet—nothing but desert.

In the days of Harun-al-Rashid, Mesopotamia had a population of between thirty and forty million (Baghdad itself had a population of two million); today the whole of Iraq has less than five million. In ancient times there was a saying, *Once upon a time the cock which crowed in Mosul could be heard in Basra.* It would be a shrill cock which could be heard over a distance of seven hundred miles, but what that saying meant was that the areas of cultivation were so closely settled (in what is now wilderness or desolation) that one cock could start a relay of crowing right down the valleys to the sea.

* * *

It is possible to stand on the hills above Carthage, in the late afternoon, and to look across the desert, and to see once again the Roman fields of two thousand years ago. When the horizontal rays of the sun, as it drops at the horizon, come across the desert, a shadowgraph of these fields reappears. From their measurements and from a survey of the ruins of fortified farmhouses which mark the frontiers of what was once Carthaginia and later the Roman province of Afrique, it is possible to estimate what the fertility of the soil (which is now desert) once maintained: the population working that soil must have been at least three times what Tunisia sustains today—and that apart from feeding the metropolis of Carthage itself—estimated at about six hundred thousand—and helping to feed the population of Roman Italy.

The story of Carthage is itself an object lesson. According to the legend it was founded by Dido, herself a fugitive from Levantine Phoenicia. To the Phoenicians, Carthage was only a trading outpost of a mercantile empire of the Mediterranean, but it became itself a proud city which excelled Tyre and challenged the aspirations of Rome itself. Its military and mercantile power was destroyed in the First and Second Punic Wars. And when Hannibal marched on Italy, his "tanks" were elephants which he found in his own back yard—in Algeria, in the Forest of the Guir, itself now only an enclave of the Sahara Desert. It was, however, the Third Punic War which has the important lesson to teach. After the Second, Carthage was destroyed as a mercantile power, and the Carthaginians had to turn upon their own resources, upon their own hinterland in Africa. Their trading ingenuity was turned to agricultural science, and there is no question that they brought into cultivation vast tracts of apparently inhospitable soil. Their agronomy became the basis of the Roman and Greek farming of North Africa for centuries afterwards. Their ingenuity was their own undoing. When Rome sent a mission of inquiry, including Cato the Elder, to intercede in a local quarrel between Carthage and its neighbor, Numidia, the Romans were appalled by the prosperity of Carthage, the rival they thought they had suppressed. When in the senate Cato declaimed *Delenda est Carthago* (Carthage must be destroyed), he waved a bunch of figs. Carthage, by its productivity, had become, not a military threat to Rome, but an economic threat to the landowning class which was beginning to develop in Italy. And so the later Carthaginians, who lived by the plow, had to perish by the plow; the victorious Romans drove a plowshare through the ruins of the Carthage they had destroyed.

* * *

The story of the Middle Eastern civilizations is largely the story of irrigation—of putting the rivers to work in a region of low seasonal rainfall. The development of Mesopotamia was due to the exploitation of the two rivers—the Euphrates and the Tigris, taking advantage of the difference of the level of these two rivers. They cut canals between them to irrigate the fertile but thirsty lands. But once you interfere with nature in this way, you have to maintain a permanent concordat, a treaty which both you and nature observe. The moment that man's artificial measures slacken, nature reasserts itself. That was what happened with the canal civilizations. There were wars which dislocated populations, and there was disease. When, for any reason, the canals became sluggish or fell into disuse, marsh conditions developed and with marshes, the mosquitoes. Alexander the Great died of malaria beside the Waters of Babylon.

The same was true of a large tract of jungle which I investigated in India. On the borders of Tibet and Nepal is the Himalayan *Terai*, the sloping ground which stretches from the foothills of the mountains to the Ganges plain. There, a thousand years ago, industrious and enlightened peasants cut irrigation canals between the tributaries of the Ganges, to extend their system of cultivation. They did not realize that they were cutting across the natural drainage of the region. The land became waterlogged. The mosquito moved in, bringing malaria which either killed or drove out the population, leaving the country to jungle in the possession of the tigers, the wild elephants, the boars, the blue oxen, the cobras and the monkeys. But, of that jungle, for a thousand years, Ping, the Mosquito, was the real king.

In Afghanistan, there is a great tract of country which lies between the Hindu Kush and the Oxus River. This is fertile land and eight hundred years ago, when Genghis Khan and his hordes, from the Asiatic Steppes, swept through, he destroyed a canal civilization. The country went to marsh. Again the mosquito moved in and made this rich land uninhabitable.

So, too, in the south of Afghanistan: Genghis' successor, Timburlane, let in the mosquito and turned productive lands to wilderness.

*　*　*

In North Africa, the decline of the great granaries was a story of the victory of the nomad—Abel's revenge on Cain. When, with the advent of Mohammedanism, the desert tribes swept through North Africa, they not only destroyed settled cultivation but the natural conditions which made that cultivation possible. The story might be summed with Hannibal's elephants. In 47 A.D., Suetonius Paulinus, before he became the general who beat Queen Boadicea and conquered Britain, was a Roman intelligence officer who surveyed North Africa and left an account of the great Forest of the Guir inhabited by all manner of wild beasts, including elephants and horned vipers. When I visited the Guir in 1950, it was bleak desert and there, at the French garrison post of Abadla, I was shown the Arab legend of Sidi Tayeb, a holy man, who appears to have been the Mohammedan Saint Patrick. It told how he was bitten by a horned viper in the Forest of the Guir and how, as he lay dying, he ordered all the animals to leave the Forest (including the elephants and the horned vipers) on six days' notice. But the footnote to the legend is the litany of the decay of North Africa: *And he bequeathed the Forest to his followers, who cut it down.*

The destruction of the forests and surface vegetation led not only to the decline of the coastal cultivation but to the disappearance of oases far south in the Sahara. The stripping of the mountains of forest cover meant that the rains, instead of seeping into the underground springs, sluiced off as surface *wadhis* and scoured off the soil.

* * *

In that apocalyptic moment in 1934, when the soil of the Dakotas darkened the sky at high noon over New York, our modern civilization was reminded of those other civilizations which had foundered in the dust of their own creation. The Dust Bowl was a warning to all men for all time. For quick returns, men had exhausted the soil of the Prairies, reduced it to dust, which was caught up and swept away by the wind. The exhaustion of the tobacco lands and the cotton lands and the gulley-scarred landscapes, and the giant floods of the great rivers, are all testaments of what happens when men are reckless in their use and abuse of the soil. The destruction of forests, overgrazing of the range lands, and overcropping of the plains bring their own penalties in disappearing homesteads. But, as the United States has shown, it is possible, with proper conservation and management, not only to arrest the devastating processes of erosion, but to restore something of the lost virtues of the land. The world has been confronted with this warning of erosion. If we ignore it, God help us. If we heed it, then not only will we correct our own abuses, but, as I can testify from areas of desert recovery, make due amends for the abuses of the past.

5. C = B : E

WILLIAM VOGT IN *Road to Survival* has given an equation— $C = B : E$.

Here, C stands for the *carrying capacity* of any area of land. It means its ability to provide food, drink and shelter for the creatures that live on it.

B means *biotic potential,* or the ability of the land to produce plants for sheltering, for clothing, and especially for feeding. Only plants are able to synthesize food from the raw materials of the earth and the air in a form on which animals can exist.

E stands for *environmental resistance,* or the limitations that any environment, including the part of it contrived and complicated by Man, places on the biotic potential.

The carrying capacity is the resultant of the ratio between the other two factors.

This formula can be applied to any area of land, whether it is the Indian's fraction of patrimonial soil, or the whole land surface of the world.

The population which it can sustain, whether animal or human, will depend upon the balance of B and E. This can be done by increasing the biotic potential, or by reducing the environmental resistance, or preferably both. Or it can be done by reducing the population which the land is supposed to feed and sustain. In a simple form, if too many animals are put out to graze on ranges of low biotic potential (sparse vegetation) and high environmental resistance (e.g., dubious rainfall), the land will be overgrazed, the plant life will be exhausted (and the biotic potential thus reduced). The soil will be eroded (and environmental resistance thus increased). The ranges will then not have the carrying capacity either for the existing overpopulation or even for a reduced population.

This formula, with its very proper warning, has been used as a defeatist argument. It has been used to endorse, and indeed to extend, the Malthusian doctrine that the population of the world will inevitably exceed the capacity of the soil to feed it. But we should in fact regard it as a challenge both to science and to wisdom, remembering that science itself is not wisdom. Science is knowledge, and wisdom is the judgment with which that knowledge is used.

*   *   *

Science can definitely increase the biotic potential. The Ancients discovered that fact when they selected seeds and began plant husbandry. Western Europe discovered that when it began properly to understand the nature of the soil. If we want to live, we have to nurse the land and find a system of doing so that builds up its fertility generation after generation. Britain boasts of such a system and can claim that farms which have been under cultivation since the Domesday Book in the time of William the Conquerer, nearly nine hundred years ago, are still rich and are yielding much greater results than they could have done then, even with modern intensive cultivation.

Yet, this system, although it is difficult to realize it, is only two hundred years old, as young as the United States itself. Through Saxon and Norman times and through the Middle Ages, right into the eighteenth century, Britain was being farmed under a system of small cultivators. The fields were worked in strips very much as is done in primitive countries—today. Under the original *Heads of Inquiry* of the now learned and august Royal Society, much emphasis was laid on the purely practical forms of farming. Knowing about the soil and the crops became a hobby of the great landlords. The turnips and the clovers were introduced into Britain, and that meant that the farms could grow far more food for livestock, especially in winter. Turnips and clover fed to livestock and manured by them were the builders of soil fertility. The system of crop rotation, consisting of clover followed by wheat, then by turnips followed by barley or oats, and then back to the beginning with clover again, created a rising cycle of fertility. More stock meant more manure. More manure meant bigger cereal crops, with more straw, from the cereals, to be trodden into more manure by the cattle, to produce still more food for man and beast. British farming reached its peak under this system in the eighteenth and nineteenth centuries.

In the twentieth century British farmers have learned a great deal about grass. In ten months they can establish a pasture which it formerly took ten years to create, and this led to a system of plowing up pastures at quite short intervals—about three years— so as to put back into the soil the manure of the animals which had grazed on it, together with the humus and organic matter and the nitrogen stored in the clover roots.

6.   THE GHOST OF MALTHUS

WHEN THE REVEREND THOMAS MALTHUS, at the end of the eighteenth century, was giving his warning about the population outstripping the capacity of the soil to feed it, he was obsessed by the multiplying humans of the new industrial society. His pertinent predictions (pertinent, but unfortunate, because they were used to discourage social advance in the nineteenth century) were countered during that century by the opening up of the new lands in North and South America, in South Africa, in Australia and in New Zealand. These new lands fed the teeming industrial populations of Europe, which he had foreseen would exceed the carrying capacity of the soil of their own countries.

On the eve of the twentieth century, another somber warning was given. Sir William Crookes, the chemist, as president of the British Association, predicted that, unless the chemists could do something about it, the world's nitrate supply would be insufficient to maintain the fertility of the land. Crookes was not a Jeremiah; he was challenging his scientific colleagues, and within fifteen years the challenge had been completely met by Haber's discovery of the method of nitrogen-fixation from the atmosphere—an unlimited and inexhaustible supply.

But today, with the world's population half as great again as it was in Crookes's day, the earth's capacity to feed its new boarders has been increased by measures which he could not foresee. The biggest factor has been the development of the comparatively new science of plant genetics, which has made it possible to breed new types of plants capable, not only of higher yields, but of growing under conditions of climate which would have ruled them out at the beginning of the century.

The wheat belt, which once stopped about the line of eighteen-inch annual rainfall, now stretches to the twelve-inch line, and the grass belt to the eight- or ten-inch rainfall line. By applying scientific genetics to wheat, varieties have been produced with qualities of early ripening, shortness of straw and high ratio of grain to leaf required for drought and frost resistance. Wheat has been bred against rust and other diseases. In Crookes's day Canada's wheat acreage was 4,000,000, and by the 1930's it had risen to 27,000,000; Australia's had risen from 5,000,000 to 16,000,000; and Argentina's from 7,000,000 to 20,000,000. Food crops have been pushed far beyond what were supposed to be the "natural boundaries" fifty years ago. They have been pushed into subarctic conditions and into the hot, arid desert regions. Hybridization and modern methods of corn production have meant that instead of the three or four bushels of corn produced by the Mexican Indian, the Iowan farmer can produce fifty bushels.

Although rice is the basic food of the larger proportion of the world's population, surprisingly little research has been done on it. Seventy per cent of the Asian people depend on rice as their staple diet, and it is there that the population is multiplying fastest. An International Rice Research Station has been set up at Cuttack, in Orissa, India, with the Indian Government as the host, with the United Nations Food and Agriculture Organization as the sponsor, and with ten rice countries cooperating. The object is to find a high-yielding rice. They are crossbreeding the *japonica* and *indica* varieties, and what is involved is apparent from the following comparative yields, in pounds of rice per acre, of the two types:

JAPONICA	Lbs. per acre	INDICA	Lbs. per acre
Japan	2,352	*Java*	1,034
Egypt	1,890	*Thailand*	888
Korea	1,593	*Burma*	816
China	1,549	*India*	772
U. S. A.	1,390	*Philippines*	703
Indo-China	716		

From this it will be seen that the yield from *japonica* in Japan is three times as great as that of *indica* in India, and more than twice that of Java, where the rice husbandry is exceptionally good. There may, of course, be many other factors besides good seed, such as better methods of cultivation, to account for part of the high yields. But the disparity between the various countries is wide enough to establish the definite superiority of *japonica*. There is, however, no question of just taking the *japonica* and transplanting it into Southeast Asia. It is the rice of the high latitudes, with more temperate conditions and longer days during the growing season, while *indica* is the rice of tropical and equatorial Asia. The northern variety is strong in the straw and can carry heavier heads. The tropical variety is weak in the straw, so that if, as has been tried, fertilizers produce heavier ears, the plants droop. The problem, therefore, is to secure, by the hybridization of the two varieties, plants which will be capable of carrying heavier ears and at the same time of being locally adapted to the conditions of the various countries.

The rewards of these researches may be enormous—as high, maybe, as the opening up of new continents in the past. If, for example, a suitable hybrid could be produced for India, it is theoretically possible to double the yield from the existing acreages and to have 30 million more tons of rice a year, which would completely transform the precarious food situation of that country.

At Cuttack they are working on other means of increasing rice yields, by breeding varieties resistant to plant diseases and to plant pests and by developing methods of fertilizing the rice soils. The Bengal famine of 1943 was produced by the failure of the rice harvest, caused by fungus disease, leading to the loss in some areas of ninety per cent of the crop. Pests, like the gallfly, attack growing crops and can destroy an entire harvest. But the scientists have found that this gallfly, under tropical conditions, attacks young plants only in four weeks in September and October. By planting early in spring, the rice can dodge the gallfly, which, with its occupation gone, will die out. The borer-grub, on the other hand, attacks in two stages; it kills the early plants, and those which are attacked in the later stages lose their grain ears. Some rice plants are mildly scented; the borer-grub does not mind but the gallfly is repelled by them; so by the trick of switching the varieties the pests can be frustrated. It has also been found that parboiled rice seeds, while not losing their virility, are less susceptible to pests.

Research is also going on into green manures for the cultivation of rice. This means sowing some leguminous plant in the rice field and plowing it in. But there are also developments in the artificial fertilizing of rice. These in the past have been discouraging, but it is now known why. It has been found that the soil in the waterlogged paddy fields has a chemical reaction quite different from that of dry soil in response to fertilizers. Instead of putting the fertilizers in the upper layers of the soil, it is plowed into the deeper layers and has produced with quite normal varieties of rice a twenty-seven per cent increase in yield.

* * *

Today plant breeders no longer confine their choice to the variations among types with which nature has provided them.

They can produce entirely artificial types by chemical treatments, for example, with colchicine, an extract of the Autumn Crocus, and by bombardment with X rays or with atomic particles. Plant breeders are beginning to know much more about the reasons why a plant can withstand drought, or cold, or disease, so that it will no longer be a hit-or-miss process; it will be a matter of custom-tailoring of plants to suit precisely the conditions in which food has to be grown.

7. THE WAR ON PESTS

JUST AS GREAT CONTRIBUTIONS OF SCIENCE to farming and to food production are the advances in pest control. When men began to interfere with the soil, they started a war which has gone on ever since. This seven-thousand-year war is against pests. It began because as soon as men became farmers and produced large amounts of food for themselves, they also produced conditions in which other unwanted animal species and plant species can thrive and multiply. Such species as the locusts, the rats and the rabbit and many weeds and parasitic fungi were quite rare until our ancestors gave them a new motive for life.

One of the most formidable of all menaces is the locust. At least one of the seven locust species is found in every inhabited continent, and the area of their activities is spreading. Until about thirty years ago, no one knew where these locusts came from or why they made their unpredictable attacks. Then it was found simultaneously in Russia and South Africa that locusts exist in two phases. In one phase they look just like ordinary grasshoppers and are harmless, but sometimes these grasshoppers go through a drastic change in appearance and behavior. They develop powerful wings, they assemble in great numbers like the hordes of Genghis Khan, and finally they take to the air. During the years 1929 to 1934, nearly the whole of Africa was attacked by locust swarms, and every one of these swarms came from one small area, near the Middle Niger. The next outbreak period was from 1942 to 1947—critical years when Africa and the Middle East were helping to feed large armies—but there were no large-scale losses caused by locusts anywhere in Africa. This can be credited to an international organization, in which all the governments, including

Soviet Russia, likely to be involved by the attacks, cooperated. The organization kept watch on all the outbreak areas and could predict the outbreaks before they occurred. The swarms were then attacked before they became airborne, with the use of poisoned baits or by spraying from aircraft. It is known now that locusts themselves are the result of unwise cultivation and that their eventual defeat will come only by large-scale reclamation of the outbreak areas.

In the early days of the settlement of Australia, enterprising settlers unwisely introduced the European rabbit. This rabbit had no natural enemies in the Antipodes, so that it multiplied with the promiscuous abandon characteristic of rabbits. It overran a whole continent. It caused devastation by burrowing and by devouring the herbage which might have maintained millions of sheep and cattle. Scientists discovered that this particular variety of rabbit (and apparently no other animal) was susceptible to a fatal virus disease, *myxomatosis*. By infecting animals and letting them loose in the burrows, local epidemics of this disease could be created. Later it was found that there was a type of mosquito which acted as the carrier of this disease and passed it on to the rabbits. So while the rest of the world was trying to get rid of mosquitoes, Australia was encouraging this one. It effectively spread the disease all over the continent and drastically reduced the rabbit population. It later became apparent that rabbits were developing a degree of resistance to the disease, so that the rabbit population was unlikely to be completely exterminated. There were hopes, however, that the problem of the rabbit would become manageable.

Ironically, Europe, which had bequeathed the rabbit as a pest to Australia, acquired this manmade disease as a pestilence. A French physician decided to get rid of the wild rabbits on his own estate and introduced *myxomatosis*. It did not, however, remain within the confines of his estate. It spread through France, where wild rabbits are not generally regarded as a pest but as a sport and a useful food supply, and it spread to Britain, where wild rabbits are regarded as a pest but where domesticated rabbits, equally susceptible to the disease, are the basis of a profitable fur industry. The question became one of whether Man could control the disease he had invented.

This example, both of the rabbit becoming a plague and of the disease, to control it, becoming a menace, has a moral for all scientists. Only by the full understanding of the ecology of the plant or animal which is being introduced, so that it is held in the true balance of nature, can innovations be successfully introduced.

This is true for the introduction of insecticides such as DDT, which are liable to kill off not only the insect pests but also the benevolent insects, like the pollinating bees, or the predatory insects which themselves control the unbalanced multiplication of other insects; or the selective weed killers; or the new systematic pesticides, by which plants themselves, by being inoculated with one chemical, can successfully produce biologically another chemical to kill particular pests which feed upon such plants; or drugs like the antibiotics, which are liable to produce new strains of germs which are resistant to these antibiotics. Scientists are well aware of this new "Theory of Unnatural Selection," which requires eternal vigilance and "ringing the changes" on the new weapons at Man's disposal.

8. FROZEN ANCESTORS

IN THE WORLD OF ANIMAL HUSBANDRY Man is beginning to acquire uncanny powers. By natural breeding, i.e., the selecting and cross-breeding of existing types, he has in a century changed the character of our domestic animals. Whereas the yield of a native cow in an underdeveloped country may be as low as a quart of milk a day, the average yield in advanced countries is two gallons a day, and yields of one thousand to twelve hundred gallons per year per cow for a whole herd are not uncommon.

But today "animal-engineering" can control even the physiology of the animals, so that milk can be produced, not only from virgin cows, but even from male animals.

The ovary of a newborn calf contains some seventy thousand eggs, but rarely do even the best of our cows produce more than ten calves in their lifetime. By the use of hormones, more eggs can be produced and transplanted into other females. Pilot experiments with rabbits showed that eighty per cent of the transplanted eggs produced normal young at birth. Using a similar technique, Willard and others in the U. S. A. obtained three calves from five eggs transplanted by this method. As this technique is perfected, it will be possible for a modern jet plane to export anywhere in the world, as fertilized eggs, whole herds of pedigree cattle for as many cents as it now costs dollars for a single animal.

The use of "prenatal foster mothers," by which animals can give birth to offspring they never conceived, has fantastic possibilities. The male sperm can now be preserved in deep freeze indefinitely. By artificial insemination it is possible for a cow or a mare to give birth to progeny, the father of which has been dead for years. Or it is possible to inseminate a pedigree cow and to transplant the ovum into a scrub animal which will give birth to a pedigree calf, unrelated to the animal which gave it birth. If, as is likely, the female ovum can be similarly preserved for a long period and transplanted and fertilized by male sperm similarly preserved, generations will be born out of their time.

By giving electric light after dark during the winter months mares can be made to breed earlier in the spring, and by giving more darkness during the summer months, ewes can be made to produce lambs in the late summer and autumn. Hens can be made to lay eggs merely by a sudden flash of light in the middle of the night. All this is caused by the effect of lighting on the glands of the animals. This is modern exploitation of the natural provision by which nature insured that animals would not give birth at times when seasonal conditions might endanger the survival of the offspring. Today science can provide the ideal, if unnatural, seasonal conditions. It is to be hoped that scientists who are gaining this kind of control are also ensuring that the liberties they are taking with nature will not be resented and produce ill-consequences. There must be a catch somewhere!

9. FOOD FROM THE DESERT

ONE THING, HOWEVER, IS CERTAIN; that our growing knowledge of the processes of nature has introduced into the $C = B : E$ equation variables, which Man can influence, and which should at least temper pessimism about the relation of population to food production. As the soil conservation measures in America have shown, those forms of environmental resistance which the greed and stupidity of men may produce can be prevented and, where they have happened, redeemed in some measure. The Dust Bowl today, with wise management, and large-scale conservation measures, is more productive than it was before the dust-laden wind gave its warning in 1934.

The world has awakened to the dangers of erosion and to the destructive effects of mismanagement. Mistakes can be turned to account. What Man did in folly for example, in North Africa and the Middle East, Man in wisdom, can undo. It means re-forestation and revegetation of what are now barren tracts. But it can be done and it can restore the forest complex and check the movement of the advancing desert. In the island of Cyprus, for example, the mere imposition of a law forbidding the free ranging goat, that destructive animal, meant a resurrection of the cypress forests. In other parts of the Middle East, the introduction of such imported trees as the eucalyptus or the acacia, which can find their own water depth, can help to restore the forest complex in which the indigenous trees and shrubs can again flourish.

This reclamation of desert is likely to be one of the most re-warding campaigns of modern science and technology. There are 18,500,000 square miles of deserts in the world, a third of the land surface. Hundreds of millions of acres of those deserts can become fertile merely by the introduction of water, either from underground sources or by irrigation. For example, under the North Saharian Desert extends the Albienne Nappe, a great water-bearing layer, in places four thousand feet thick. It is a great reservoir, replenished by the rains of the Atlas Mountains. Soundings have been sunk into it, which have proved its extent and its water-bearing capacity. At Zelfana, in Algeria, the layer was reached at about one thousand feet depth and produced a "gusher" one hundred feet high. This water is now supplying a considerable agricultural colony in the desert. That is only a beginning. Similar sinkings are being made over a wide area of the Sahara to establish artificial oases. To quote the French scientist in charge, "Life is being brought to a howling desert."

There are millions of acres of desert in Pakistan and in India which are being brought into fertile production. The Negev in Israel, half the area of the new state, is being developed, and crops have been won from what was only a few years ago a bleak desolation of the Biblical wilderness. It was estimated at a symposium of world experts on deserts held in Jerusalem in 1952 that, without even contemplating the vast areas of remoter deserts which could be made fertile, there were 200 million acres of accessible deserts which could be economically developed by irrigation now.

Extensive studies have been undertaken of the nature of desert plants and how, by transfer and adaptation, plants from one part of the world could be introduced to meet the needs of other parts. New studies have been started on the phenomenon of dew—a factor which has been strangely neglected, when one considers the enormous significance attached to dew by the Ancients and expressed in the Old Testament. It has been found, for instance, by Professor F. Went, of the Californian Institute of Technology, and by Dr. S. Duvdevani, of Israel, both from field experiments in Israel and laboratory experiments in California, that certain plants, even in a rainless desert, absorb in a night more dew than they need and secrete it into the soil. It should be possible, by selecting such plants, to produce an excess of moisture in the soil to supply other selected plants which have not got this dew-absorbing capacity.

Similarly, a great deal has been learned about the phenomenon which always mystifies desert travelers—the sudden blazing into life of colorful flowers in deserts where there may have been no rain for ten or fifteen years. At the first substantial rain, desert seeds sprout and blossom. The explanation is an "inhibitor," a chemical which prevents their growth. It is a sort of chemical mackintosh. If there is merely a skirmish of rain which would be insufficient to bring the plants to maturity, some of the "inhibitor" may be washed off, but the seed will regenerate it and go to sleep again until there is sufficient rain to make it grow.

Similarly, desert trees and shrubs, once established, exude from their roots an inhibitor into the soil, which will prevent any seeds around from growing. This is the shrubs' way of staking out its catchment area, reserving to itself the moisture necessary for its own growth. But if there is a sufficiently heavy shower which will wash out the inhibitor from the soil, it will be enough both for the established shrub and for the sleeping seeds. And they will come to life.

The nature of these inhibitors is now known, and with knowledge and ingenuity it ought to be possible to treat seeds and disseminate them—if necessary from the air—over areas of the desert. They will lie dormant until there is rain enough for them to root. It is one way of revegetating the wastelands.

10. FOOD FROM THE JUNGLE

ON ANOTHER JOURNEY WHICH I MADE for the United Nations I was concerned with jungle. Tropical vegetation is abundant, but its very abundance may be deceptive if we should recklessly try to clear it for open cultivation. The exposed soil may perish by being dried by the sun or being sluiced by the rains. Nevertheless, it is possible with proper management to bring into cultivation for human benefit vast areas of what are now called jungle. The story of many of these jungles is the story of the Himalayan Terai— once cultivated regions which had to be abandoned owing to malaria. Once the malaria is cleared, as it has been in the Terai and in other parts of India, it is possible to establish food cultivation provided the balance of nature is preserved. This can be done by careful ecological study. For example, in the Terai, although there are 1,700 million acres of jungle now liberated from malaria, the region will never be cultivated to its full extent because large parts of it are being protected as forest—as reserves for wild animals, but also to ensure that the forest acts as a sponge to trap the rain, which might otherwise sluice off the soil, and seep the water into the underground springs.

Even in terms of what has been called "climatic suitability for crop growth," this world of ours is still underdeveloped. It is estimated that 11,000 million acres come within this conservation description—conservative, that is, because by adaptation of plants, difficulties of climate can be overcome. But of that area less than 4,000 million acres, or less than ten per cent of the world's land surface, are at present cultivated. Of this total, the food-producing area represents about one and a half acres per head of our population. But another three and a half acres per head might be brought into cultivation.

11. THE CHALLENGE

HERE, THEN, IS THE GREAT CHALLENGE. The world population problem is now difficult, but in the next fifty years may become catastrophic. The population by 1975 cannot be less than 3,000 million, and may be more. Science, and animal and plant husbandry, combined with the techniques of modern mechanization, could still feed such numbers—and feed them better than is the lot of two-thirds of the population now. It cannot be done by the thoughtless exploitation of nature; that would mean merely destroying the prospects of future generations. It can, however, be done by the wise application of the knowledge we have and the knowledge we are acquiring.

A wise man has said, "Live as if you would die tomorrow; farm as if you would live forever."

Science
and
Industry

. . . Broadly speaking, there has not been a time during the past fifty years when anything manufactured by the General Electric Company was not, to some extent, at least, obsolete by the time it was put in service. . . .

OWEN YOUNG, on the speed of change at the G. E. C. 50th Anniversary Meeting

Science and Industry

1. MILLIONS OF MEN WITH TEASPOONS

THE USUAL CROWD OF ONLOOKERS were gathered round the rim of a city-crater. The giant excavator was scooping out the deep foundations of the building-to-be. Its iron jaws were biting off rocks and rubble by the tons and spewing them into enormous trucks. This was in The Years of the Bread Line.

Said one unemployed man, bitterly: "If it wasn't for that blankety-blank machine, there would be work for hundreds of men with picks and shovels."

Said another bystander: "Or for millions of men with tea-spoons."

*   *   *

I recalled this incident when I was in the mountains of Central Java. The scene was vastly different. There, under the equatorial sun, naked brown bodies were sweltering in the heat, cutting a canal, which, eventually, would be forty miles long. They had no equipment except their own muscles, mattocks and scoops, hammers and chisels. In this way, the Babylonian slaves must have cut the Hillah Canal, diverting the Euphrates. With such freaks of muscular effort, the Javanese ancestors of the present-day workers must have built fabulous Borobudur, the great Hindu pyramid temple in this same region.

When they encountered volcanic rocks, they just chiseled their way through. They would chip the rock and then drive in wedges to rive it apart. Then they would break it into pieces small enough for the bearers to carry away on their heads. They filled baskets with spoil and, like copper-colored gnomes in some weird fairy tale, the bearers would scamper up the long, swaying bamboo ladders to tip their few pounds of muck and scurry back again. In a year they had advanced two miles through the volcanic mountains.

Modern science had given them one thing—the health and strength to undertake this strenuous enterprise. For there, in the mountains of Kulumprogo, seven out of every ten people had been afflicted with that dreadful disease, yaws, or frambesia. One injection of penicillin could drive the disease out of their bodies, allow the ulcerous scars to heal and give them new strength and new purpose. And part of that purpose was to bring rice into those thirsty mountains where the staple diet was cassava and plantains. This canal along the mountains was to bring the water which would cascade down the hillsides flooding the terraces where the rice would grow.

But I thought that modern science ought to give them more than just physical well-being; it ought to give them gelignite to shift, in minutes, the rocks which it took weeks to chisel and break; it might have given them bulldozers to shift that muck and conveyor belts to replace those scurrying bearers. And I protested in those terms to the United Nations officials with whom I was dealing, but one of them, a good scientist and a wise man, scolded me. "Don't even suggest it!" he said. "This is *their* canal. For the first time, they will have something they do not owe to the moneylenders, who have held whole generations in pawn. If you were to make the offer of equipment, they would never believe you were disinterested; they'd think it just another device of the moneylenders. No, let them make it their way. It is their fulfillment."

2. MACHINES VERSUS MEN

To the Western worker on the bread line, the Machine was the first threat to his livelihood; to those Javanese peasants, had they but known it, the Machine could have provided their livelihood and given them, more quickly, the rice they so desperately wanted and needed.

And, of course, the remark about "millions of men with teaspoons" was justified; the relevance of men to the machines is relative. There can be no turning the clock back (or even turning the clock into a sandglass), because a technological civilization has changed its sense of values and its proportionate measurements.

If we were to convert modern units of energy back into muscle power, it would need the entire male population of New York, or

London, to row a great modern liner across the Atlantic; it would require the entire population of the world—2,400,000,000 people —to provide muscle power equivalent to the energy output of the United States electrical power stations; and conversely, a few thousand men, with dynamite to quarry the stone, power-cutters to shape the blocks, tractors to haul them and giant cranes to hoist them, could build, in two or three years, the Giant Pyramid which, it is estimated, kept over 100,000 slaves employed for twenty years.

Yet the fear of The Machine persists, less, perhaps, in the United States, where an industrial society grew up with The Machine, than in other societies, where it conflicted with traditional ways. Men cannot get used to the idea that it is their servant and not their master. The distrust does not now take the form of the excesses found in the early days of the Industrial Revolution, when Hargreaves' home was invaded and his spinning jennies destroyed; when Arkwright's new machines for carding, roving and spinning were systematically wrecked and the British Parliament was petitioned to ban them because the worker's plight was "so intolerable as to reduce them to Despair and many thousands assembled in different Parts to destroy The Causes of Their Distresse"; when Jacquard's looms for weaving brocaded silks were destroyed and their inventor "delivered to ignominy"; and when Barthélemy Thimmonier's sewing machines led to rioting in Paris. But there is a genuine fear on the part of craftsmen that modern mechanical and electronic devices will not only rob them of their trade but of their skills within that trade. For example, the traditional steel makers have only with reluctance accepted instrumentation which does not replace their skills but makes the skilled worker the more skillful—quite apart from increased output and increased wages.

* * *

Bertrand Russell has argued (*Impact of Science on Society*) that the American Civil War would "almost certainly not have occurred if cotton had remained unscientific."

> At the time of the War of Independence [he argues] and for many years after its close, the Southern States were quite willing to contemplate the abolition of slavery in the near future. Slavery in the North and West was abolished by a

unanimous vote in 1787, and Jefferson, not without reason, hoped to see it abolished in the South. But in the year 1793, Whitney invented the cotton-gin which enabled a Negro to clean fifty pounds of fibres instead of only one, as formerly. "Labor-saving" devices in England had caused children to have to work fifteen hours a day; labor-saving devices in America inflicted upon slaves a life of toil far more severe than what they had had to endure before Mr. Whitney's invention. The slave trade having been abolished in 1808, the immense increase in the cultivation of cotton after that date had been made possible by importing slaves from the less southerly states where cotton was not grown. The deep South was unhealthy, and the slaves on the cotton-plantations were cruelly overworked. The less southern slave states thus became breeding ground for the profitable southern graveyards.

As a comment on this it may be worth pointing out that it was beginning to be apparent about 1850 that slave labor was less profitable than "free" labor. For this reason slavery might have languished and died without the Civil War. But the political issue of high tariff and free trade would have remained. The Northern mills wanted high tariffs to exclude the competition of British cotton goods. The Southern planters wanted free trade. The policy of high tariffs, to protect the home market, is the direct result of Whitney's cotton-gin.

3. SLAVE ELECTRONS

THE NINETEENTH CENTURY SAW THE REPLACEMENT of muscle by metal, human energy by steam and, in the last part, by the internal combustion engine. The twentieth century has been a more subtle, a more far-reaching, change—the artifaction of the human senses and to a degree not to be exaggerated, of the human brain. Never was an adjective more ironically applied than that of "free" to the electron; for it is our most complete and abject slave. "Electrons" are the basis of another industrial revolution, for they move faster than human reactions and are less subject to (but not entirely free from) temperament. They "see" more than the human eye, "feel" more sensitively than the human touch, "hear" more than the human ear and "count" more accurately and faster than the human brain. So far we have not satisfactorily reproduced the senses of taste or smell—or we might have "tele-gustation" and "teleolfaction" as well as teleaudition and television, and "smellies" as well as "talkies." Both may come, although as Dr. E. D. Adrian, who received the Nobel Prize for his work on the nervous system, has shown, the cells of the smell sense, which transform the chemical essences into electric pulses to the brain, are more diversified and complex than the brain cells themselves.

In industry, the development of electronic instruments and servomotors has made it possible for massive and complicated processes to be taken over by automatic or semiautomatic ma-chinery, with a minimum of workers. At the one end of the scale is the handling of thousands of tons of steel in the rolling mills; at the other, the "printing" of complicated circuits for radio sets.

A modern rolling mill is a fantastic place in which metal is processed with the speed of newspapers rushing through the printing presses. At every stage, instruments stand guard, gauging and maintaining the thickness of the plate, automatically adjust-ing when any variation occurs. Devices can detect flaws in a sheet moving with a speed which would defeat the human eye. Ahead of this process are the blast furnaces in which the steelmakers have been given additional senses, like the photoelectric device, which enable them to regulate the furnaces with an accuracy (and con-fidence) so that twenty per cent more steel can be produced than when it was necessary to depend on the most expert verdict of the human eye. And beyond are the giant presses which can stamp that steel sheeting into automobile bodies.

Anyone who has ever tried to make a radio set knows what a finicky and complex process it can be. But electronics has made it possible for two girl workers to produce sets at the rate of *one every twenty seconds.* Known as "Electronic Circuit-Making Equipment" it consists of two batteries seventy feet long. Each battery is a series of fully automatic machines governed by elec-tronic devices. The process starts with a molded plastic panel in which the whole wiring system—the inductance coils, condensers, resistors and conductors—are just grooves in the flat surface; it looks like a diagram of a radio circuit such as one might see in a technical magazine. The panel is then sprayed with metal so that there is a fine deposit over it all and the indentations are filled. It is then milled so that the layer is removed from the flat surface, but the indentations are filled. It now looks like a picture stenciled in metal, and the threadlike "canal" on the original surface is now an unbroken wire. A zigzag is now a fine coil, and a condenser has been formed by using the plastic as the dielectric. Machines fix on the terminals and plug in the valves. Wiring mistakes cannot happen because the human fitter who might connect the wrong wires has been eliminated, and there is no need even for a human inspector, since an electronic device will discard any faulty panel. The machines can run day and night so long as there is a worker to feed in the materials at one end and collect them at the other. This business of stenciling circuits surprises us only because we have got used to the idea that electricity must pass through wires which we can handle, like thread, but, of course, the electrons are just as happy buzzing through any continuous layer of metal. With the development of transistors, such methods can give us more and more diminutive sets. Transistors are those remarkable devices, smaller than a fingernail, which can replace conventional radio tubes. These transistors are a throwback to the "cats' whiskers" of the early days of broadcasting. Then, with a feeler and a crystal and earphones clamped on the ears, the pioneers groped for the fitful transmissions. The modern device employes a tiny flake of geranium crystal, with fixed "whiskers," and forms a powerful, practically indestructible and long-lived equivalent of the radio tube.

4. ELECTRONS DON'T PAY UNION DUES

THE EXAMPLE OF THE STENCILED CIRCUIT shows how the applied scientist, the designer and the process engineer can bypass the mechanic, just as the pressed-steel body displaced the coachbuilder, and the plastic molds mass-produced the skills of the furniture maker. It is at this level of completely new processes, and not in the invasion by the machine of the established worshops, that the artisan must come to terms with science.

The operative phrase is "come to terms," because manifestly science is going to go on changing the pattern of industry, and to hinder it would be as futile as the efforts of Dame Partington to sweep back the waters of the Atlantic. This requires a great deal of understanding and participation by organized labor. This was recognized by the British Association for the Advancement of Science when, in 1937, it approached the British Trades Union Congress and proposed a Joint Committee of scientists and leaders of the unions. (This was in the spirit of the charter of the B.A.A.S. —"to remove the obstacles which would stand in the way of the advancement of science.") The offer was welcomed by Mr. Ernest Bevin, later British Foreign Secretary, and then chairman of the T.U.C. The intentions of the scientists were quite clear: they wanted to survey, with the workers, the trends of science which would affect the nature of employment and, from their knowledge of what was already happening in the laboratories, to forewarn the unions of the changes so that they would not suddenly be confronted by convulsive changes and resultant frictions; they would have time to adapt the attitude of their members to the changing pattern of employment and, indeed, adapt their own union structure, to meet and to accept the changes to their advantage rather than their hurt.

Perhaps the attempt was premature, since the committee never functioned properly and died at the outbreak of World War II. The war, itself, brought about drastic changes in the structure and location of industry, and, instead of large-scale unemployment, there was a shortage of labor which made the extension of machine methods and instrumentation imperative. It also produced joint consultative committees of employers and labor in which the adoption of scientific methods was fully discussed and agreed at factory level.

5. OPERATIONS RESEARCH

ONE OF THE DEVELOPMENTS OF THE WAR was "Operational Research," something more fundamental than "scientific management" and "time-and-motion" study, which, in Britain at least, had been a cause of violent friction between labor and management. "Operational Research," or "Operations Research," is the application of scientific method, not necessarily to a single operation, but to an organization. The organization may be an assembly shop, or it may be the running of government or a complicated sector of society. (It was applied successfully to the Medicine Murders in Basutoland, where Operational Research showed that the outbreak had been caused by insecurity leading to a reversion to ritual murders to appease the ancestral gods. But it all arose from social reforms and tax adjustments intended to benefit, but misunderstood by, the Basuto tribesmen.) Simply expressed, it is the re-examination of traditional methods and attitudes.

It is perhaps best illustrated by wartime applications. In 1941, I went to see a friend of mine, a geneticist, who was working in a basement laboratory at Aberdeen University. He was most excited. He was counting the hairs on the antennae of the *drosophila* (the banana fly) and had found a mutation—extra whiskers—on the progeny of parents which he had fed on Vitamin B. Pretty remote from the life-or-death struggle which had followed the retreat from Dunkirk and the Battle of Britain! The next time I heard of him, he had doubled the flying capacity of Coastal Command, the air command responsible for the protection of the supply lines to beleaguered Britain. And he had done it *without adding a man to the personnel or a machine to the air strength.*

* * *

Coastal Command had been given one of Churchill's famous half-page chits ordering them, without reinforcements (because they were not available) to increase the patrols over the Biscay Ports, from which the U-boats were operating against Atlantic shipping with devastating effect. It seemed to be asking the impossible, but the problem was given, as his first assignment, to this geneticist, Dr. Cecil Gordon, who had been assigned to "O.R." He had no status, just a licensed buffoon whose novelty amused the Officers' Mess, and he was "humored" by the personnel as he went around asking silly questions. And "silly" they must have appeared, because he had never seen the intestines of an aircraft engine nor flown in an aircraft. He just "stooged around" talking to people, asking them *what* they were doing, *how* they were doing it and *why* they were doing it. They knew "what" and "how," but very often they did not know "why."

Gordon treated Coastal Command as though it were a colony of his pet *drosophila*. He applied the scientific method—observations; hypothesis, based on these observations; theory, evolved from checking the hypothesis, experimental proof of the theory and finally a "law." In this case, the immediate outcome was not the promulgation of a "law" but the rescinding of one. The "law," in this case, was an Air Force ordinance known as "The Co-efficient of Serviceability."

By peacetime organizational standards, the efficiency of an Air Force Station was judged by the number of serviceable aircraft—not in the air but able to fly; in other words, not undergoing maintenance. Now the *reductio ad absurdum* of serviceability is never to put an aircraft into the air, because after so many hours it becomes due for servicing. Aircraft were certainly flying on rigorous patrols, but the Book of Rules—the accretion of peacetime practices—required that seventy-five per cent of them must be "serviceable." Spelled out like this it seems ridiculous, but, of course, it was not so directly obvious. The geneticist, with only a pencil and paper, found the answer. It meant a modification of "The Co-efficient of Serviceability"; drastic reconstruction of the ground organization; and changes in the flying schedules. It "loosened things up," not to the impairment of flying efficiency but to the improvement, and it made no unreasonable demands on the flight crews. The number of patrols increased, equal to twice as many machines from the factories which could not produce them; twice as many air crews, who would have had to be recruited and trained; and a substantial reduction of the ground staff. The secondary "law" which he introduced was "Planned Flying and Planned Maintenance." With the introduction of the new regime, six weeks after the geneticist had begun his "look-see," the U-boat "kills" by Coastal Command were doubled. An important feature (and one indispensable in Operational Research) of this affair was that the findings were not imposed from the top by the Air Council, but were first accepted at "ground level" by the officers and men of the air station and went up from them (not from the scientist) to the higher commands.

*   *   *

Operational Research began in Britain with the faults found with radar. The scientists who produced the radar equipment and the engineers who made it were satisfied with the performance before the instruments left the bench, but the results, in practice, did not prove so satisfactory. Sir Robert Watson-Watt decided to send his physicists on to the antiaircraft sites and into the military establishments that were using the equipment. He thought, at first, that it was merely a matter of instruction or of finding physical reasons (for instance, it was found that long grass round the radar-detectors was producing interference, and the answer was wire-matting or just sheep). As it happened, however, mechanical trouble had little to do with it. Often it was just a human problem —an unpopular battery commander, a poor mail service or just too little sugar in the canteen tea—or organization.

The classic instance was the Case of the Extra Man. The scientists inquiring into the problems of the antiaircraft batteries found it difficult to account for one man on the strength of each gun. It turned out that he was "the man who held the head of the horse"—a leftover from the days of horse artillery.

From such humble beginnings, the penetration of science into military organization grew to be of decisive importance. Every command, naval, air and army, had its "Tame Magicians." They were attached to the Chiefs of Staff and the Strategical Planners. Their findings were applied in the planning of convoys, the hunting of U-boats, the bombing of Germany in land battles. "The Theory of Combat," which was one of the products of "O.R.," worked effectively on sea and in the air and to a more modified extent in land warfare. "The Theory of Combat" for land battles was perfectly all right on paper, but it had to assume as a "constant" what in fact was a "variable"—the infallibility of generals!

* * *

When America entered the war, Operational Research was developed and extended on an increasing scale and in a great variety of circumstances. And when Admiral Doenitz, faced with the failure of the U-boat "blitz" on Atlantic shipping and the build-up for the liberation of Europe, sent his despairing signal to the Führer, "We have lost the U-boat war because the enemy used science and we did not," he was referring not to the anti-U-boat gadgets but to the systematic application of scientific method in tactics and strategy.

Military "hunches" and "Fortunes of War" were reduced to measurements. As Professor P. M. S. Blackett, the British Nobel-Prize winner, who was awarded the U. S. Medal of Merit for his pre-eminent part in this work, wrote in a document which laid down the principles "of O.R.":

> Many war operations involve considerations with which scientists are specially trained to compete and in which serving officers in general are not trained. This is especially the case with all those aspects of operations into which probability considerations and the theory of error enter. . . . The scientist can encourage numerical thinking on operational matters and so avoid running war by gusts of emotion. (See *Scientists Against Time,* the official history of U.S. O.S.R.D. James Phinney Baxter 3rd.)

The principles of Operational Research, so successful in war, are valid in peace. They demand the scientific method and the objectivity of the scientists applied not only to productivity, but to industrial relations and to social problems. It is particularly relevant to the ironing out of the problems involved in the transitions of industry brought about by new discoveries, new materials, new processes, new sources of power and the new industrial and new social conditions which ensue.

6. COMING TO TERMS WITH THE MACHINE

CIRCUMSTANCES, OF COURSE, CHANGE, and considerations which at one moment seem intransigent become amenable. In The Hungry Thirties, the British coal miner was definitely hostile to science so far as it affected his job. He resisted even the introduction of fluorescent lighting at the coalface, because it meant that one man in sixteen would become redundant. He resisted the introduction of machinery because it would mean fewer men with picks ("or millions of men with toothpicks"). All that has changed. The British miners' complaint today is that his mechanical auxiliaries are not being enlisted fast enough. For social reasons, again hinging on the miners, the electrification of railways and the introduction of diesel-electric locomotives were discouraged on British railways because it would reduce the demand for the product of the mining industry with so many chronically unemployed. Nowadays, the National Coal Board, with the full support of the Miner's Union, is attacking the railways, the electrical power stations, industry, and the housewife, for their wasteful use of coal!

When, after the war, the coal industry was finding it difficult to recruit youngsters, one of the reasons was that the miners were discouraging their sons from going into the mining industry "because there's no future in it." There was, on their argument, no future because, within a generation, atomic energy would have displaced coal as a primary source of power. That attitude changed. Atomic energy came to be regarded, not as a competitor, but as a partner. By February, 1954, the Chairman of the British National Coal Board could say: "The danger is that atomic energy will not come soon enough to take the load off coal. I can see no danger that it will come too soon—the sooner the better. Coal will still be needed as the raw material for carbonization and for chemicals." The British Electricity Authority, at the same time, was actively sponsoring the development of industrial atomic-reactors—and not for the reason that in the United States the processing of atomic materials was utilizing as much electricity as the entire output, for all purposes, of the British electrical generating stations, but because by 1960 the power stations would be needing thirteen million tons, and by 1970, sixty-three million tons more coal than the mines would be producing. So the British miners, at least, had come to terms with the greatest scientific advance of all time—the release of atomic energy.

In the meantime, the atom industry in the United States had become the rival in size, certainly in capital invested, and probably in workers employed, to the biggest of the older industrial corporations. Its ramifications reached into many other industries as well. And that in less than fifteen years after Otto Hahn and Strassman observed uranium fission.

7. THE SPEED OF CHANGE

WHAT AMERICAN TECHNOLOGY ACHIEVED in the five years following the announcement of uranium fission was, in its own way, as significant as the atomic energy which was released or the atomic bomb which was exploded, because it changed the time-scale of progress. To realize just what this means one should consider the following from S. C. Giffillan's article, "Prediction of Invention," in *Technological Trends,* a prewar U. S. Government report:

Taking the 19 inventions voted the most useful, introduced between 1888 and 1913, the average intervals were: Between when the invention was merely thought of, and the first working model or patent, 176 years; thence to the first practical use, 24 years; thence to commercial success, 14 years; to important use, 12 years—say, 50 years from the first serious work on the invention. Again in the study of the most important inventions of the generation before 1930, the median lapse was found to be 33 years between the "conception date," corresponding to the second above, and the date of commercial success. Searching for exceptions, it is hardly possible to find an invention which became important in less than ten years from the time it, or some fully equivalent substitute, was worked out and few did it in less than 20 years."

Apply the same scale to atomic energy: We can take $E = MC^2$ —Einstein's theoretical prediction—in 1905 as the base line; if we accept Cockcroft and Walton's atom-smasher, Chadwick's neutron and the Joliot-Curies' artificial radiation (all 1932) as the "serious work" on disintegration, that would give us 27 years instead of 176; but the release of atomic energy did not, in fact, become a practical proposition until Hahn's discovery in late 1938, so we can count it as 33 years instead of 176. But, after that, comes the fantastic telescoping of time: from the "first working model or patent" to "important use" (let us agree that Hiroshima and Nagasaki constitute "important use") gives us only five years, of which it was the last three which really mattered.

From fifty years to five! From two hundred and twenty-six to forty! Forty years to work out the combination of Nature's basic vault and five years to turn a fundamental discovery into a bomb!

Behind the regiment of great scientists were the corps of technologists, men and women experienced in the large-scale conversion of laboratory ideas into industrial practice, and behind them again were the armies of workers, skilled and unskilled, who could be recruited from a population of 134,000,000, and behind those again the wealth which could spend $1,500,000,000 in less than three years on an experiment, which was not put to the proof until Alamogordo, until July 16, 1945; which could take $70,000,000 worth of silver from the caves of the Federal Bank and turn it into wire for coils; and, above all, the imagination which refused to be balked by any project, however outsized or seemingly farfetched.

8. THE ATOM GOES TO WORK

THIS EXPENSIVELY ENDOWED AND RAPIDLY PRODUCED "know-how" was the massive secret which the United States wanted to safeguard at the end of the war; this "know-how" was to give it and the Western World strategical strength; and the McMahon Act confined that knowledge to the United States itself. Without minimizing the question of espionage, scientists, including those of the United States, knew that the idea of monopolizing the "know-how" was self-deception. It was only a matter of time before other technologically developed nations would acquire that, *or other,* "know-how"—because the real secret exploded at Los Alamos and, for all the world to know, at Hiroshima and Nagasaki. That secret was that it was possible to release atomic energy. That much known, it was only a matter of a few years, this or that side of five years, before the same effect could be reproduced elsewhere.

And so it happened. Russia got first the fission bomb and then a thermonuclear reaction. Britain, although its scientists had participated fully in the physics of the Manhattan Project, but had not taken a full part in the technology, was excluded from any share of the know-how by the McMahon Act. That meant a seven years' delay in demonstrating, at Monte Bello Islands, Australia, that Britain could reproduce the bomb. But in that time Britain had created large factories to process uranium and produce fissionable materials; it had worked out the elaborate safety precautions (one of the big factors in the delay because all this was taking place in a densely populated island); its chemists, working with a pinhead quantity of plutonium—twenty milligrams—produced at the Chalk River Project in Canada (at a time when the United States was stockpiling plutonium by the kilo) had to discover the methods of separation and, on the strength of twenty milligrams, go ahead with huge plants; and it had to redo all the experimental work on the atomic piles. But by 1954, Britain was in the atomic energy business in a big way.

And there was considerable urgency in the British industrial energy programs for reasons which did not apply in the same way to the United States, which had one overriding priority—the production of atomic armaments. The reasons in Britain were more concerned with energy, both for domestic use and as the basis of future exports. In America, with its vast resources of coal, oil, natural gas and hydroelectricity, industrial energy was a *desideratum* rather than an imperative. But in Britain there was practically a deadline—a deficiency of thirteen million tons of coal for power generation by 1960.

The first domestic use of atomic energy was claimed at Harwell, the British Atomic Research Station, on November 19, 1951, when the buildings were heated by the heat-residue of the atomic piles. But on the walls of the power-plant room of the U. S. Reactor Testing Station, in Idaho, appears the historic message: "Electricity was first generated here from atomic energy on December 20th, 1951." Both of these innovations were but the by-product of other activities; reactor stations, designed for the primary purpose of producing industrial power, were still to come.

In the spring of 1953, the British Government announced that work had begun on such a station at Calder Hall in Cumberland. The reactor was to be a natural uranium pile, such as that used for converting uranium into plutonium. In the spring of 1954, work was begun at Dounreay, in the far north of Scotland on the site for a "breeder pile" to be based on the experience of "Zephyr," the fast-reactor which became "critical" (i.e., functioning) in

January, 1954. A "breeder pile" is a reactor designed to produce more atomic fuel than it consumes, while, in this instance, producing heat to be transferred to turbines to generate electricity. In principle, it means that a fast-reactor forms the core, like a fierce furnace, but it is enclosed in an envelope of either uranium, to be converted into plutonium, or thorium, to be converted into Uranium 233. The conversion is done by the escape into the surrounding material of neutrons, the atomic particles which enter the nuclei of atoms and make them radioactive. Breeding, in short, is a process of producing more plutonium in a reactor which is "burning" plutonium, and surrounded by Uranium 238, or of producing more Uranium 233, in a reactor which is burning Uranium 233 but surrounded by thorium.

Such power-breeders are likely to form the backbone of any future atomic energy power system, and the British program predicts that in twenty years efficient power-breeders will have been developed to a point at which they can be built in sufficient numbers to achieve the goal—the generation of all Britain's electricity. But, in the interim, the program provides for the extension of the "converter-reactors" (like the natural uranium one being constructed at Calder Hall) which will feed electricity into the national grid sufficient to meet the coal deficit. In addition, these converters will be producing the plutonium for the initial fueling of the breeder piles.

9. ATOMIC POWER FOR UNDERDEVELOPED COUNTRIES

ENDLESS AND INEVITABLE CONTROVERSY goes on about the economics of power reactors for industrial purposes, because it is difficult to work out costs when, so far, the dominant considerations have been military and costs a charge upon the nation. Billions of dollars have been invested from national funds in the production plants from which industrial installations will derive their initial supplies of fission fuel. The capital costs of reactor plants are vastly greater than equivalent steam-generation stations, but once stoked with fuel and efficiently maintained, a converter station might run for thirty years without refueling (but it would need "decoking" because it can stifle itself with radioactive by-products). A breeder station, if it fulfilled the scientists' promise, would pay fuel dividends. Sir John Cockcroft, head of Britain's atomic research, has declared that "the cost will not be in excess of the cost of producing electricity from coal."

It is the fact that, once established, atomic power-stations do not need transport services to maintain constant and massive supplies of fuel—railway tracks to carry coal or pipelines to carry oil or natural gas. And this is what makes their development of such importance to power-hungry countries. These countries are mainly the underdeveloped countries looking for short cuts to industrialization. And because they are underdeveloped and lack communications and/or coal, oil or water power for hydro-electricity, they want plants which can be established in isolation—oases of industry. Some of these countries, notably Canada, Australia, South Africa, Central Africa, India and Brazil have a special claim—they are the countries which provide the ores from which fissionable materials are obtained and which the "atom" countries, U.S.A. and Britain and the U.S.S.R., lack in the quantities they require. Nor are these countries likely to accept relegation to the role of "primary producers," just the miners of materials.

This has been recognized by American authorities, like Mr. Thomas Murray, of the Atomic Energy Commission, when he said that more disturbing than the news that Russia had the H-bomb would have been the announcement that it had developed industrial "know-how" and would be prepared to trade it for political and economic advantages and raw materials.

Leaving aside the definitive question as to whether an atomic war will ever be attempted, the release of atomic energy with its vast possibilities of peaceful use has changed, or can change, the industrial pattern of the world.

Science and the Family

. . . That ruthless Juggernaut, the needs of man. . . .
THOMAS ALVA EDISON

Science and the Family

1. THE ATOM COMES TO DINNER

"PLASTICS!" EXCLAIMED MY HOSTESS DISGUSTEDLY, eyeing a particularly obnoxious ornament from Aunt Martha. "I wish they had never been invented."

"Sshh!" I cautioned. "Polly might hear you."

"Who's 'Polly'?" she asked.

"Why, Polymer, of course," I said shamelessly. "Polymer is the fairy godmother of plastics and she might grant you your wish. And then think what would happen!" And I told her:

She would be standing there stark naked because her dress and (I suspected) her foundation garments, her nylon stockings and her party slippers were all from artificial resins. There would be a mess on the carpet because the tray on which she was serving the cocktails was plastic. The television set would be a naked chassis because the cabinet was plastic. The telephone would be a heap of metal parts. Her curtains of vivid synthetics would have vanished. The plastic finish would have peeled off the walls and the doors. The electric-light switches would have disintegrated, and the apartment would be in darkness because the tube lighting would have crashed when the holders disappeared. The molded table would have crumbled. Nine-tenths of Junior's toys would have gone and most of her kitchen fittings. The apartment would be flooded because, being a modern building, the pipes were of polythene. And, of course, the house would be on fire because all the electric wiring had been insulated with plastic.

* * *

Because it has all happened so quickly and we have accepted it so nonchalantly, we do not realize how completely science has invaded our homes. Nor how much more it will invade it in the future. Most of us take it for granted, without even understanding what it is all about—like the woman, at another party, who overheard us talking about the domestic use of atomic energy.

"Nonsense!" she protested. "I wouldn't have an atom in the house. Scientists ought to have something better to do than go around inventing atoms!"

"Excuse me, Mrs. Postlethwaite," I interposed, "but you are sitting on an atom." She squeaked and leaped out of her chair, as though there was an atom bomb underneath. I then had to explain all about atoms. How everything was made up of atoms— her chair, herself, the air she was breathing and the Manhattan she was drinking.

And I had to go on and explain that atomic energy would come into her home completely tamed and fully house-trained. What such people do not realize is that atomic energy, which exploded with such unprecedented violence at Alamogordo and with such destructive effect at Hiroshima and Nagasaki, can be strictly disciplined.

In an atomic pile or reactor, the atom is the fuel of a new kind of furnace, not one which derives from chemical combustion but from physical disruption. The pixie is the *neutron,* that ghost particle which, penetrating the powerful defenses of the nucleus of the atom, causes it to split and release energy. The trick which converts uranium into plutonium and releases energy in the process is to get enough of these neutrons splitting enough atoms. But just enough—if too many are split simultaneously, that is a bomb. The reactor is swarming with neutrons which are diverted into the uranium by what is called a *moderator,* which may be pure graphite or heavy water; in either case it acts like the cushion of a billiard table. When the neutrons are too active and the fission process too fierce, steel rods containing boron or cadmium are pushed in to absorb the surplus neutrons and keep them out of mischief.

The splitting atoms produce heat in the reactor and this heat has to be removed, whether for useful purposes or not, because it can become excessive to the safety of the pile. The removal can be done either by water or by liquid metal or by gas, circulating in a closed circuit from which the heat is exchanged with another circuit, which, this time, uses the steam or hot gases to drive the turbine of an electricity generator. From there on, "atomic energy" is just ordinary electricity. In the home it will respond to the usual switches, light the lamps, operate the vacuum cleaner, make the ice cream, grill the chop and work the television set. The day atomic energy comes into her home, Mrs. Postlethwaite will not recognize her new domestic help; it will be indistinguishable from her old one.

2. THE PRESENT FROM THE PAST

IN EVERY ASPECT OF ORDINARY LIFE, science's presence is taken for granted. Things now commonplace, for instance, soapless detergents (or, for that matter, soap itself), are quite extraordinary. Imagine going back all those millions of years to the primeval swamps where oil began, just to remove grease from a twentieth-century plate! Think of "detergent," and then think of "Surface Tension," that exercise of pure science which explains the "skin" on a blob of grease or on a drop of water, and then think of the chemists who, through the oil refineries which gave us gasoline for automobiles and aircraft, for central heating and for cigarette lighters, presented us with something which can "make water wetter" and enable it to overcome the surface tension of the grease. Think back to the primitive man killing the beast for its pelt and forward to the present when we can make nylon stockings out of the forests and sludge which were there before he was and which now give us coal and oil. Think of curing a headache with aspirin, which nature had "prescribed" in the elements of the Carboniferous Age before the human brain that has the headache ever existed.

It is difficult to realize that a hundred years ago the production of aluminum was negligible and that our familiar pots and pans had to wait for electricity and the discovery that aluminum could be extracted from an oxide-cryolite bath by electrolysis (1888). Or that magnesium, discovered by Davy and first extracted electrolytically by Faraday, remained a laboratory curiosity practically until this generation. Or that such metals as beryllium, titanium, germanium, or zirconium became recognizable as names only in the Atomic Age.

Or glance in the larder at the canned foods. Or into the refrigerator at the frozen foods. Or pick up a packet of dehydrated vegetables. And remember that they have been with us only since yesterday.

* * *

If that hostess had said, "Begone science!" and a fairy godmother had taken her at her word, practically everything which she considers to be "everyday things" would have vanished. And the apartment block itself would have collapsed because constructional steel and concrete would have disappeared, too.

This is the trouble: ordinary people blame science for the fears it has introduced—the atom bomb, the guided missile, the long-range bomber, biological warfare and the like—and forget the benefits like our domestic amenities or like penicillin and the antibiotics which have probably saved more millions of people than modern war has destroyed.

3. HEALTH FOR THE HOME

MORE IMPORTANT TO THE FAMILY, and to the individual, than all the gadgets of the home which science has provided, is the contribution of science to health.

Consider and contrast the conditions in your own country a century ago with those of today. Or think of the contemporary world around you and the appalling state of the people in the underdeveloped territories compared with those of the technically advanced.

In Bengal, in the Ganges Delta, one child is born every minute and one child dies every ninety seconds. Throughout Southeast Asia and parts of Latin America one child in every three dies before the age of one year; four out of every five suffer from chronic disease; and the average span of life is under thirty years compared with the present expectation of life, in Western countries, of nearly seventy years. It is difficult to realize that this is not far removed from the picture of Britain or America in the days of Charles Dickens.

The change has not been entirely due to the "miracle drugs," the White Man's Magic provided by the chemists and medical scientists of our own generation. We are too liable to make that assumption mainly because it is the spectacular short-cut remedies which make the headlines while the great services in the background do not. But it is essential to remember what we owe to the preventive public-health services which we now (ungratefully) take for granted.

The public-health movement, the recognition of health as a social responsibility, dates from about 1850, when the Sanitarian Revolution was just beginning to make its impact. There was the growing insistence on clean water and proper sewage systems, the safeguarding of food supplies and the creation of facilities for the isolation of communicable diseases—the lazaret and the quarantine hulk. Next emerged positive "Preventive Medicine," with the discovery of satisfactory methods in bacteriology, vaccines and sera, and of epidemiology and vital statistics, which provided us with intelligence about the disposition of the forces of the enemies we were attacking. In this phase came the demand for services to look after the health of school children, industrial workers and mothers and infants, and for protection as well as for attack. Next came the scientific phase, which provided the technical and pharmacological means to deal with individual diseases, infectious and noninfectious; to the vaccines and sera (mobilizing the defenses of the body) have been added the chemotherapeutic drugs such as the sulfas and the antibiotics, which have given doctors the means of attacking, selectively and directly, the specific causes of specific diseases. Insecticides such as D.D.T. have greatly strengthened the means of indirect attack, intercepting and destroying the carriers of disease (such as the mosquito, with its bomb bays loaded with malaria or yellow fever). Concurrently with these advances there has been the development of the science of nutrition and of social—and industrial—psychology, which directed attention to Man's environment. All these are so much an accepted part of civilized existence in prosperous societies that we forget how comparatively recently they have emerged.

4. THE ABC OF VITAMINS

IT IS DIFFICULT FOR ANYONE of the younger generation to realize, for instance, that our knowledge of vitamins is no older than the twentieth-century. We owe the word (with the discarded final "e") to Funk (1912), but the Nobel Prize for the discovery of vitamins was awarded jointly to the Englishman Sir Frederick Gowland Hopkins and the Dutchman Christiaan Eijkman. Hopkins, in 1906, published a paper based on long experimental work in which he said:

> There is still an unknown substance in milk which even in very small quantities is of paramount importance to nutrition. If this substance is absent, the organism loses the power properly to assimilate the well-known principal parts of food, appetite is lost and amidst abundance animals die of want. Undoubtedly this substance occurs not only in milk but in all sorts of foodstuffs both of vegetable and animal origin.

* * *

The story of Eijkman is more picturesque. He had been sent by his government to the East Indies to investigate the ravages of beriberi amongst the native population. The mission decided it was an infection, but Eijkman was not satisfied with the report (although he accepted the germ theory) and stayed behind to try to "isolate the germ." One day, he noticed some fowls in a hospital yard, with a peculiar limpness of neck, droopiness of the wings and wobbliness of the legs, and his scientifically trained mind immediately recognized that here, in fowls, was the human affliction of beriberi. He also discovered that the fowls were fed on the leavings of the food served to the beriberi patients. His first hypothesis was that the food was carrying the germs from humans to the poultry, and he proceeded to carry out bacteriological tests. His experiments were rudely interrupted when an officious new superintendent of hospitals found that the fowls were being fed on milled rice (i.e., with bran removed) and ordered them to be given unmilled rice. Eijkman protested that they were now his experimental birds, but he was rudely rebuffed with the reply that the mission had ruled that the disease was caused by human infection, and that to pursue his poultry experiments further was a waste of public money.

So the fowls were given the crude rice, which was regarded as not good enough for hospital patients and, as far as the disconsolate Eijkman was concerned, his experiments were scuttled.

Then one day going past the poultry-run, he saw that the fowls were "perking up" and, later, that they were normal. So he posed himself a second hypothesis. Was there something in the milling of rice which caused beriberi? He studied the medical records of prisoners fed on unpolished rice. In thirty-seven prisons, unpolished rice was served, and in only one was there a case of beriberi. In fifty-one prisons, polished rice was served and in thirty-six of them beriberi was rife. But, such was the influence of Pasteur and Koch, the vogue of that time, that he still believed that beriberi was a germ disease and that the substance in the bran was just the antidote. In 1906, the year of Hopkins' announcement, he revised his opinion and declared, "There is present in rice polishings a substance of a different nature from proteins, fats or salts, which is indispensable to health and the lack of which causes nutritional polyneuritis."

*　*　*

Such statements at that time were heretical, because scientific and, indeed, popular thinking was still dominated by nineteenth-century "mechanism" and the chemical cocksureness of Liebig, whose disciples thought they had "all the answers." The chemists thought of the body as an engine for which carbohydrates were the fuel and the proteins were the repair and maintenance accessories. Based on those and on essential minerals, baby foods had been produced and had become fashionable. The well-to-do mothers who previously, when they were unable to suckle their babies, had hired that humble but obliging creature, the wet nurse, could now have Balanced Bottles for Bouncing Babies—infant foods, based on the confident prescription of the "ideal food." Their babies "bounced" all right: they were fat and podgy, but they developed "Barlow's Disease," which is infantile scurvy (caused by the lack of Vitamin C) and rickets (caused by the lack of Vitamin D) and latent forms of other deficiency diseases. It has been said that Hopkins saved the British upper classes from disaster because his "accessory food factors" reminded scientists of Claude Bernard's wise injunction, "When in ignorance, refrain."

5. THE CASE HISTORY OF B_{12}

THE DISCOVERY THAT THERE WERE ELUSIVE FACTORS in natural foods which were missing in the most thorough synthetic diet started the intensive search which still goes on. An alphabet of vitamins has grown, and in the case of that complex Vitamin, B, we have now reached B_{12}, the most powerful physiological factor known to Man.

This vitamin has an interesting case history which, properly, should go back to 1849, when Thomas Addison at Guy's Hospital, London, described a "remarkable form of anemia . . . without previous loss of blood and no malignant disease." This became known as "pernicious anemia," which is caused by the failure of the marrow of the bone—the blood factory of the body—to produce enough red blood cells. To do this, the marrow has to obtain some chemical from the stomach and this, in the pernicious anemia patient, is lacking.

Before 1925, any patient with the disease was under sentence of death; he might survive four years at the longest. But in that year, a young Boston physician, Dr. George R. Minot, formed the hypothesis that the anemia victims did not eat enough meat and, with his colleague, Dr. William P. Murphy, he began to feed them with the most concentrated form of protein—liver. To ensure that none of the value was lost, they made them eat it in raw form, minced. It was a nauseating diet, but it worked; pernicious anemia patients became well and stayed well so long as they maintained their raw-liver diet. The disease was no longer a killer.

Because of the unapalatable nature of the diet, however, the search went on for more highly concentrated and less objectionable forms. In 1948 the answer was found in Vitamin B_{12}, and it was found simultaneously in Britain and America. It was what scientists call a "beautiful discovery." The chemists used chromatography. This is the method which exploits the fact that constitutent chemicals in a compound diffuse through certain materials at a different rate. The simplest example is the "halo" around an ink stain on a piece of blotting paper and, indeed, absorbent paper is one of the devices of the chromatographer. In this case, however, an absorbent mineral was used in a glass column. The liver extract was allowed to filter through, each constitutent chemical traveling as far as its molecular weight would take it and then stopping. One separated out as a thin red line, which was cut out and examined. It was what we now know as B_{12}. When tried on human patients it proved thousands of times more potent in pernicious anemia than any other treatment.

While clinical tests were proceeding slowly in Britain, the American experimenters took a short cut. They tested it on a germ culture of *lactobacillus,* which is the bacterium which sours milk and which Dr. Mary Shore, of Maryland University, had found to react to the pernicious anemia factor. With this confirmation, the American results were announced a fortnight before the British. And it was a great discovery—a three-millionth of a gram can restore the stomach juices, revive the marrow and set the red blood cells into circulation. It is no longer necessary to obtain it from the liver; it is a by-product of antibiotic manufacture.

* * *

In such ways, research is constantly and rapidly adding to our knowledge of the nature of vitamins, enzymes, hormones and other biological chemicals. The relationship between those chemicals which are ingested by the body from outside sources in the form of food and those manifold chemicals which the body itself produces is being clarified. But our knowledge is still incomplete and our ignorance should always give us pause. When Gowland Hopkins was eighty years of age, and accepted all over the world as the outstanding biochemist of his time, he said to me, "Everything I have ever learned about vitamins and every new one discovered reminds me of what I do not know. Vitamins are units of ignorance rather than of knowledge."

6. THE CAUTIONARY TALE OF CORTISONE

THERE IS IN THAT STATEMENT the humility of wisdom which should temper the avidity with which the public seizes upon each new medical advance as though it were the final answer. A classic example was the tremendous popular acclaim and excited headlines which followed the announcement of the discovery of cortisone. In fairness, it was not only the public but the scientists and doctors as well who became excited by the indications of a drug which would cure rheumatoid arthritis, that disease which cripples millions—seven million in the United States and two million in Britain.

Nor do the second thoughts on cortisone and A.C.T.H. diminish the importance of the work for which Dr. Philip S. Hench and Dr. Edward Kendall, of the Mayo Clinic, and Professor T. Reichstein, the Swiss, were awarded the Nobel Prize in 1950. Rather they give the discovery a new significance.

Dr. Hench, in 1929, had noticed that men and women with arthritis had less pain when they had jaundice and that women, expecting babies, often had their rheumatism relieved and that rheumatic patients who had surgical operations for other reasons were also temporarily benefited. Here was a piece of observation. What common factor was present in these three, very different, circumstances?

The scientists speculated whether in the adrenal *cortex* there might not be a still unknown "Substance X" which would prove to be the anti-rheumatic factor, because the secretions from the outer layer or *cortex* of the adrenal glands on top of the kidneys are particularly active in jaundice, in childbirth and in surgical operations.

After years of biochemical research, Compound E was extracted from the adrenal glands of cattle. It could also be extracted from bile, which provided the link with jaundice. In 1949 the first cases were treated and the results were certainly dramatic. Patients who had been completely bedridden, with crippled joints, and unable to move, let alone walk, were out of bed within a few days. Within a week, under treatment, pain and muscular stiffness had disappeared and the patients could literally dance a jig with relief. But it was not a "cure," any more than insulin is a "cure" for diabetes and, like diabetes, rheumatism could only be kept in hand as long as regular injections of Compound E were given. The moment the injections were stopped, the patients relapsed into their previous condition, worsened, in fact, by the feeling of temporary well-being they had experienced.

Similar effects could be obtained by means of A.C.T.H., obtained from the pituitary gland which lies in the middle of the head at the base of the brain and controls all the other glands. A.C.T.H. is obtained from the anterior lobe of this pealike gland, and it is this lobe which controls the adrenals. Remove it and the glands on the kidneys shrivel. Restore it by transplantation or by injections of A.C.T.H. and the adrenals function again. In the rheumatic cases, A.C.T.H. encouraged the adrenals to produce the deficient cortisone.

But there are other effects which disquieted the doctors and made them wary about this treatment of arthritis. It was liable to produce "hirsutism," the growth of whiskers on women's faces, and other male characteristics in women. Either cortisone or A.C.T.H. will stop an attack of gout, but if either is given in quiet periods the gout flares up. Actual infections are checked, but quiescent infections are encouraged. It gives temporary relief to cases of high blood pressure, but the salt content in the tissues rises, showing that the relief is only temporary. So one contradiction after another has manifested itself, moderating, while not discouraging, enthusiasm for these ambiguous drugs.

7. THE CLUE TO THE WORRY DISEASES

RESEARCH HAS GONE ON. The drugs themselves have been improved and cheapened and many have benefited. While the earlier claims have been tempered, newer claims have been made, and they may have a meaning far beyond rheumatism, important though that may be. A complete new line of thought and investigation has been opened up which may find many of the answers to the degenerative diseases and stress diseases which are the price we are paying for our advancing civilization.

Oversimplified, the arguments run something like this: the pituitary reacts to the mental and nervous system. The hormones (such as A.C.T.H.), which it sends out, stimulate the other glands, notably the adrenals. The adrenals, by a series of chemical messengers, stimulate the body processes—including the stomach acids which, in excess, give us gastric ulcers, or the sugars which, in excess and unchecked by insulin, give us diabetes, or the salts, which, in excess, cause thickening of the arteries and high blood pressure, thrombosis and heart trouble. In certain circumstances, the lack of the secretions from the adrenals caused the "gumming up" of our joints in painful arthritis, because that part of the chemical processes of the body which keeps our joints "oiled" is not functioning because of a deficiency of cortisone. What the discovery of cortisone and Kendall's Compound F and A.C.T.H. has done is to open up a new field of inquiry into the action of the hormones, in response to the stresses and strains imposed upon our minds, nervous systems and body functions. It is at least as important a point of departure as the discovery of vitamins at the beginning of the century.

These two examples—vitamins and cortisone—have been given to show that knowledge of the *nature* of the chemistry of the body is even more important than the individual discoveries of particular items and corrects the all-too-ready assumption that such-and-such is the answer. Glib acceptance leads to vogues and cults, spectacular successes and crashing disappointments. But a recognition that such-and-such is only the part of a bigger picture means that the doctor is conscious of The Whole Man and in ignorance he will refrain, or in awareness, pursue. Put another way, the science of nutrition, which tells us what our healthy diet should be, is more important than the individual vitamin which may cure a deficiency.

And important as such things as insulin and cortisone may be when wisely used for treatment, they may be more important in leading us to a positive answer to the problems of degenerative diseases—the challenge to medical science in the second half of the twentieth century.

8. MID-CENTURY MEDICAL CHECKUP

THE TIME HAS, IN FACT, come when we need a medical stocktaking. Diseases might be classified under three categories—mass diseases, degenerative diseases and diseases of stress. "Mass diseases" can be used to describe those diseases which are so widespread in a community and affect so high a proportion of the population as to be a dominant factor in hindering the social and economic developments of the country, and which, medically, mask other diseases to the point of making them clinically irrelevant until the mass diseases have been removed.

The mass diseases by this definition may be regarded as the tangle, the jungle undergrowth of disease, which has to be cleared before a country has a fair chance of development. When it is cleared, other forms of ill-health reveal themselves, as they have done in the highly developed countries.

Mass diseases are: malaria, tuberculosis, bilharziasis, yaws, hookworm, syphilis, trachoma, gastrointestinal diseases and diseases of malnutrition. Pestilential diseases—cholera, smallpox, bubonic plague, typhus, typhoid and yellow fever—would rank as "mass diseases" in epidemic form, since they would affect, kill or disable, substantial proportions of the populations. But these pestilential diseases by and large have been brought within the manageable limits of public health.

Insect-borne mass diseases, like malaria, can be controlled by modern methods, such as DDT spraying, and at a relatively small cost of between fifteen cents to fifty cents per head of the affected population. Person-to-person diseases, such as syphilis and yaws, can be combated with penicillin, costing less than twenty-five cents per head of cases treated. Tuberculosis, another person-to-person disease, can be restrained by inoculations of B.C.G., by which a mild strain of tubercle bacillus (Bacillus Calmette Guerin) injected into a person free from tuberculosis may produce an immunity. The emphasis is on "restrain," because a B.C.G. campaign does not, like DDT, destroy the carrier of the disease, nor, like penicillin in yaws and syphilis, cure the victim; it merely assists in protecting a proportion of those likely to be disposed to tuberculosis infection in communities still ridden with tuberculosis. In individual cases, for certain forms of tuberculosis, the new antibiotics in combination with the sulfa drugs can be successful in helping sufferers. But the effective way of reducing tuberculosis as a mass disease can only be by social improvement attacking the conditions which propagate the disease.

Only when the mass diseases have been reduced and cleared away does the social and medical significance of other diseases become apparent and comparative statistics begin to have some meaning. The case of Ceylon is one in point: for centuries the major cause of death and illness was malaria. Chronic malaria existed in two-thirds of the island and flared up into epidemics.

9. "EASTERN" BECOMES "WESTERN"

IN 1934, AN EPIDEMIC OF MALARIA affected one-fifth of the island of Ceylon. The immediate cause was the prolonged drought caused by the late arrival of the southwest monsoon. The pools of water in the dried river beds formed the breeding grounds for the mosquitoes, and the spread of the disease was favored and magnified by the gross undernourishment of the population. Deaths from malaria in 1935 rose 3,400 per cent compared with 1933. In 1946 DDT spraying was begun and as a result, the malaria sickness rate dropped by 77.5 per cent between 1946 and 1949, and the death rate from malaria dropped by 82.5 per cent. This was accompanied by a marked reduction, in total deaths, in infant mortality, in maternal mortality and in some of the other major causes of death. To quote H. Cullumbine, "The Analysis of the Vital Statistics of Ceylon." (*The Ceylon Journal of Medical Sciences, VII,* Parts 3 and 4, p. 120.)

In the space of one year the total mortality rate fell from one typical of Asian countries generally to a level comparable with the more prosperous and advanced countries of the West. This reduction in the death rate has been accompanied by an alteration in the principal causes of death. Although one in every nine is due to parasitic and infectious disease and only one in twenty to cardio-vascular diseases (diseases of the blood circulation system), there are definite signs that the mortality picture is becoming "westernized."

"Westernized" in this case means that the degenerative diseases are becoming apparent. The degenerative diseases are mainly those associated with the old-age groups—diseases of the heart and circulation, brain hemorrhages, organic and glandular disorders (e.g., diabetes) and cancers. Diseases of the heart and circulation system and cancers and tumors now account for over fifty per cent of all deaths in the countries with the highest *per capita incomes.* The increase in these diseases can mainly be attributed to the extension of the expectation of life. People in the advanced countries now survive long enough to have these diseases, whereas in the under-developed countries, they are killed off by the mass diseases before the degenerative diseases reveal themselves. It is in the area of the degenerative diseases that the new medical advances must come.

10. THE PRICE OF PROGRESS

THE DEGENERATIVE DISEASES ARE, FOR THE MOMENT, the price which we are paying for the benefits which science has conferred in extending the span of life.

The "diseases of stress," however, are the price that we are paying, apparently, for the material advantages of our scientific and technological civilization. The speed and strain of modern living, the fears and conflicts of competitive advance, are reacting on the human body. Gastric and duodenal ulcers, now increasingly common in the advanced countries, are examples of such "stress" diseases, and there are plain indications that what were formerly regarded as diseases of the aging, such as arteriosclerosis and thrombosis, are being thrust back, as stress diseases, into the younger age groups. Statistically the extent of mental ill-health in advanced countries looks ominous. The amount of the increase is deceptive, because of better diagnoses and better statistics, and because of the increasing recognition, by doctors, of nervous and mental conditions which a few years ago would have been neglected or ignored in their early stages. Even allowing for the *apparent* increase, there is undoubtedly a real increase in neuroses associated with the stress of modern life. By this reference, alcoholism is a "stress" disease, although it would appear merely to be the drowning of symptoms of neurotic disorder.

If we are concerned with the future of our species and the well-being of our children, we have to confront these new manifestations and to recognize the paradox that while science has given us control of the diseases of our environment, and the means to defeat the germs which attack us from without, science is also helping to create, in other ways, conditions of life which are reacting on the mind and body.

More than ever before, "the proper study of mankind is Man."

PART

7

Science
and
Society

The wise seek knowledge and action as one:
They seek truly.
Take either path
And tread it to the end:
The end is the same,
There the followers of action
Meet the seekers after knowledge
In equal freedom. . . .

BHAGAVAD-GITA

Science and Society

1. RIP VAN WINKLE COMES TO TOWN

CONSIDER THE CHANGES WHICH Rip Van Winkle would see if, having drunk an extra-strong potion in the Catskills a hundred years ago, he were to wake up in the world of today.

When he went to sleep, modern science and nineteenth-century technology were barely hinting at the marvels to come. There were "iron horses," the steam locomotives, riding the trails to the West, in spite of the pulpit denunciations of them because they had not been foretold in the Bible. There were steamboats plying the Hudson, a venture once derided as "Fulton's Folly." There was the telegraph, although when Morse ten years before had asked for a government appropriation of $30,000 for an experimental line, he got it by a margin of only eight votes, because some of the opposition wanted to give an allocation to mesmerism instead. There was gaslight in the cities, although William Murdock (another member of The Lunar Society) had been described by Sir Walter Scott as "that madman who is proposing to light the streets of London with smoke!" If Rip used oil lamps in the Catskills, the fuel would be either vegetable oils or whale oil, because kerosene and Drake's oil strike in Pennsylvania were still to come in 1859.

There were no electric generators nor electric lamps; the first skyscraper (Home Insurance Building, Chicago) was still thirty years off, waiting for constructional steel and elevators to be developed; no bicycles; no automobiles; no streetcars; no airplanes; no telephones; no phonographs; no celluloid for film and no movies; no talkies; no television; no X-ray photographs; no general use of anesthetics (doctors were still skeptical about Long, Morton, Warren and Simpson, who had adventured with ether and chloroform in the 1840's); no germs, as far as doctors knew, and so no antiseptics; no proper sewage systems nor purified water; no artificial fibers nor artificial textiles; no plastics, except vulcanized rubber; no refrigerators; no vacuum cleaners; no newsprint from wood; no dynamite; and, of course, no atom bomb.

* * *

Imagine Rip Van Winkle being found in a long-forgotten clearing, by a forest ranger, who, of course, has a walkie-talkie radio with which to call the nearest town. "Here's a guy with a long white beard," he says. "Got a keg. I reckon he's a moonshiner. Mighty queer though: he keeps asking how Franklin Pierce is making out as President. . . ." The Associated Press "stringer" in the town would (of course) realize at once that this was Rip Van Winkle. He would flash the news to New York. Within a couple of hours a flock of helicopters are dropping in on that clearing. Only to find that an enterprising television scout has already parachuted from a jet plane and put Rip Van Winkle under contract.

Before Rip is properly awake from his century sleep, he is circling round the Empire State Building in a helicopter and descending on Manhattan.

"And what, Mr. Van Winkle, do you think of our highspeed civilization?" says the television reporter, pointing to the streets of New York with the automobiles jammed, immovably, bumper to bumper.

When they land, he is snatched by a waiting ambulance and rushed, with a siren escort, to the hospital where he, the living proof of hibernation, is "given the works"—but the whole works —the sphygomannometer, to check his blood pressure; the electroencephalograph to check his brain waves; the electrocardiograph to check his heart; scopalamine and the lie detector to check his story. He is X-rayed and blood-tested. The pathologists, physiologists, endocrinologists, opthalmologists, bacteriologists, microbiologists, cytologists, gerontologists, hemotologists, osteologists, trychologists, and, naturally, the psychiatrists, all want to examine this rare specimen and, if possible, get a bit of it.

* * *

Before he is entirely vivisected, Rip Van Winkle is rescued by the attorney of the television company, waving the contract like a writ of *habeas corpus*. Twenty sponsors are already competing, including the Methuselah Vitapill Corporation; the Deepsleep Narcotics Company; Catskill Applejack Inc.; the In-Death-As-In-Life Embalmers; the Samson Hair-Restorer Corp.; and the Delilah Depilatory Corporation.

Having survived the helicopter, the ambulance and the hospital check-over, he barely survives the high-speed elevator to the forty-seventh floor and the shock of seeing and hearing himself on the television playback of the film-and-sound record of his rescue. And when he makes his studio appearance, he is more appalled by the artificial suns, in the form of electric arc lights, than by the cameras and the microphone which mean nothing at all to him. Nor can he conceivably imagine that he is being seen three thousand miles away on a coast-to-coast hookup.

After that, he does The Town. He eats ice cream for the first time, and food cooked by high frequencies or brought out of Deepfreeze. The soda jerk fascinates him even more than the subway, and pressure cooking more than the automatic telephone exchange. He has his beard permanently waved. He sees himself on 3-D, shaking hands with a phenomenon which did not exist a hundred years ago—the glamorous film star. He is taken shopping to buy suits made of artificial wool and socks made of nylon. He does not really believe them when they tell him his transparent raincoat is made of coal. In the stores he sees textiles undreamt of a century ago and colors unconceived (Perkin had not then discovered synthetic dyes). He smells odors which did not exist a hundred years ago—scents rapturously redolent of flowers but from coal just the same, and the lung-rotting fumes from car exhausts.

Plumbing fascinates him. He amuses himself for hours just flushing the toilet or running the hot-and-cold into the bath and making rain with the shower. He does not understand how his hotel room can be hot without a fire, nor the mysteries of air conditioning, nor how, when he presses a button, an elevator comes up, nor the radio announcer whose voice comes into his room when he turns a knob. Nor can he understand how electricity which grills a chop can also produce ice cubes out of a refrigerator.

They take down his Catskill Dutch conversation on a wire recorder and a typist (shameless hussy!) transcribes it on a typewriter. As a "visiting fireman" from another century he, of course, has to see a newspaper office with news being teleprinted every minute from every corner of the world, telephotos arriving from Tokyo, telephone calls from every part of the earth and the thundering rotaries swallowing miles of newsprint. He sees color printing, color movies and color television.

Of course, he is fascinated by the neon signs and moving lights, but the radiation countersignaling the flying particles of the splitting atom impresses him less than a pin-table. A jukebox enthralls him; the electronic computer leaves him cold. (This "brain," they tell him, can do in a few seconds mathematical equations which would take Ph.D.'s months or years, but since Rip could never count anyway. . . .) They fly him—for a stunt—across the Atlantic and back the same day, but he prefers Coney Island Fun-Fair.

They show him machines smashing down buildings and helping to put them up again. There is the grab which scoops up tons of muck at a bite and a bulldozer which (they tell him, but he does not believe them) is pushed by a hundred and fifty invisible horses. He sees pneumatic drills and welding machines and skyscrapers cased in glass.

Twenty million televiewers see him being introduced into the twentieth-century home, with its vacuum cleaners, washing machines, launderettes, refrigerators, television, electric sewing machines and meals-in-a-minute out of cans. And hear him being asked what Mrs. Rip Van Winkle would have thought of that. But they do not hear his reply because he is too busy playing with Junior's space-gun.

This strange eventful history of a man who went to sleep in the mid-nineteenth and woke up in the mid-twentieth could go on indefinitely. We could take him into atom factories and down into submarines and up into the stratosphere. We could, but unfortunately Nature has supervened. Rip Van Winkle could not endure the strains and stresses of this hectic age. So after a month of modern life, supercharged in his case by glandular injections, special diets, vitamin cocktails and the like, he died. The necropsy found that trademark of the twentieth century, the duodenal ulcer, but not far enough gone to account for death. The truth was probably that he died of the shock of Civil Defense rehearsal for an atom-bomb raid.

* * *

This allegory of the new Rip Van Winkle, however, may serve to remind us of the changes in the last century—that hundred years in which Man has advanced further and faster—in material achievements—than in the whole of the previous five hundred thousand years. From the discovery of Fire to the release of Atomic Energy.

All those things, which we have discussed in terms of Rip Van Winkle, and many more, are the innovations of a single century. They are the commonplaces of our existence. Father cannot imagine life without a car, yet it was not until 1885 that Daimler drove a bicycle powered by internal combustion and the first automobiles were conceived. It is barely fifty years since President Theodore Roosevelt "with characteristic courage" rode in an automobile—followed by a horse-drawn carriage in case it broke down! Mother cannot imagine the home without electricity, yet Edison's first public-supply generating station did not come into existence until 1880. The teenagers cannot imagine a world without the talkies, yet Friese-Greene's motion-picture patents belong to 1888, the sound track to 1929 and the development of color reproduction to the 1930's. Children have already become television addicts, although I can remember seeing J. L. Baird's first transmission, at the British Association in 1927, of a puppet head and of him, two years before, in carpet slippers, in an attic workshop near the Covent Garden fruitmarket in London, sending "vision" from one room to the next. No girl can imagine a world without rayon or nylon, yet there were no artificial fibers until 1893 and no nylon until Carothers synthesized polyamides in 1935.

2. THE SHRUNKEN WORLD

A TEST WHICH ONE MIGHT APPLY to the commonplace is irritation when what we take for granted lets us down. The unconscious reflex which flicks the switch in a darkened room becomes irascibly conscious when a fuse blows out. The driver frets at a minute's holdup at a crossing when the straining horses under his engine hood will do eighty miles an hour on the open highway beyond. Although airliners have reduced the time-space factor from weeks to hours, and shrunk our world to a fraction of its size, we fume because fog delays our take-off for a few hours. We chafe when there is half an hour's delay in passing a radio-telephone call which, transmitting our voice with the speed of light, 186,000 miles a second, will enable it to be heard in Berlin, or Bombay, or Brisbane, quicker than it will be heard by someone in the same room, since sound waves only travel at 750 miles an hour.

The world has shrunk because of the universality and speed of communications until there are few places that are really inaccessible. I was once traveling in the Sahara Desert hundreds of miles from "civilization" when I was overtaken by a Camel Patrol. They had a message which read, "Children say you are wrong. You say 750 miles. They say 250 miles." It had come from London to Algiers, from Algiers to Colom Bechar, from there to Beni Abbes and, forward, by radio-telephone to the outpost of the patrol. It must have mystified military intelligence, but I guessed that it referred to a dispatch which had appeared the previous day in a London newspaper. My journey was being followed day by day by schoolchildren all over Britain, and I had given latitude and longitude for the extent of one part of my journey and they had "measured me up." The reply must have been more mystifying as it went back over the same route. It was, "Tell children desert swanning does not mean crow-flying." ("Swanning" means detouring.) And there was another occasion when I was called down by radio-telephone from the Jungfraujoch—11,000 feet—to take a call from London which was merely my newspaper asking my advice about a service message they had just received from Schenectady. In Rangoon, Burma, I was introduced to three men in the hotel. "But," said one of them, "I heard you speaking tonight from London." "No, no," said the second, "I heard him. It was from Bangkok." "You're wrong," said the third, "I know he was speaking from the Rangoon radio station." But all three were right. On that one evening, I had "done" three broadcasts. One was part of a series which I had "canned" before I left London. The second I had recorded three days before in Bangkok and had sent back to London by air to be relayed back to Southeast Asia, and I had broadcasted "live" from the Rangoon studio. By modern communications one can be in three places at once!

3. JABU AND THE JUKEBOX

OF COURSE, ONE DOES NOT HAVE TO ROUSE a Rip Van Winkle to
find someone who would be staggered by modern advances. There
are maybe some people even in the Catskills who are living in the
mid-nineteenth century. There are certainly plenty in the world
who are living remote in Time and Space from science. I have met
Indians in the Mexican Sierras who know aircraft but have never
seen a wheeled vehicle. I have seen a bicycle, a beautiful chromium-
plated machine, hanging from the rafters of a long house of the
Dyaks, the Bornean ex-head-hunters, although there was not a path
in the jungle for a hundred miles around on which to ride it. I know
of other long houses to which smart salesmen have sold refrigerators
in exchange for rubber, although there is no electricity.

The shock impact of the twentieth-century (Western Time)
civilization was something I myself witnessed on a mission which
I undertook for the United Nations. It was to study the problems
of disease, hunger, ignorance and misery which it is hoped that
Technical Assistance will help to relieve. And one of the problems
was: "Resistance to change." Where better to start than among a
primitive, pagan people? So we plunged into the equatorial jungle
in Borneo and arrived at one of those Dyak long houses. It was
built in the treetops, on a great raft of bamboo slats, supported on
ironwood piles. The house was a long building which housed under
one roof two hundred and fifty people. It was dominated by a
jungle mountain on which lived Jabu, a malevolent spirit, who
sent sickness and hunger to the long house when he was displeased.

The Dyaks of this *kampong* or village were a friendly people.
They were pleased to see us, but they were not too sure that Jabu
would be likewise—particularly in view of our baggage. This included a radio-recording apparatus and lots of camera gear, flash
bulbs and the like, and typewriters. They understood none of these
things and had to consult Jabu and get his permission to receive
us. So, after a preliminary ceremony in which they tried to find
out whether Jabu would consider receiving a messenger at all, we
were hurried off to The House of the Heads. This is where they
keep the skulls which they worship. Most of the skulls were old
(head-hunting had been vigorously discouraged for fifty years),

but one of them was comparatively young. It was a Japanese head taken in the Occupation, when the White Men who had told the Dyaks that head-hunting was a wicked thing had dropped young men by parachute from the skies to tell them it was a good thing —as long as it was the White Men's enemies who were being killed! This was the head which was chosen as the messenger (as the youngest and fleetest). Rice beer was poured into its throatless mouth, and he was offered tidbits to sustain him on his way. He was harangued by the Palan Gawei, The Head of the Feast, who was almost as old as Rip Van Winkle. Then the flap of the roof was raised and, in mime, he was sent off.

The Palan Gawei then sat down and in a sort of trance began to play a reed pipe and alternately, intone. We had left our equipment outside, but at this stage we discreetly introduced the microphone and made a recording. After a long interval, the Palan Gawei, with a sprightliness which belied his years, leapt to his feet and in great excitement announced that the messenger had returned and Jabu had replied that he approved of us and that we would bring good rice and good health to the long house. To clinch it, we played back the radio-recording—our answer to Jabu. The result was extraordinary. The Palan Gawei sat absolutely paralyzed as the sound of his piping and his voice came back. This must be Jabu mocking him. Then somebody laughed and then everybody, including the Palan Gawei, laughed. And we played it again.

We could then do anything we liked—take photographs in The House of the Heads, startling them with flash bulbs, or make any recordings.

But being friends of Jabu had its disadvantages. We were Good Spirits with strong magic and we were drafted into the rituals which went on and on all through the night—including a blood ritual in which a chicken was sacrificed, and I had to splatter everyone with hot blood. Our early success then became a trial— everything had to be played back. They even wanted the photographer to play back his photographs!

From that, and other experiences in the jungle long house, I came to the conclusion that what was to be feared, for those people's own sakes, was not resistance to change but the too ready acceptance of it. These people might be head-worshiping pagan animists. Their livelihood, dependent on the whims of Jabu, inferior rice seed and primitive cultivation, might be precarious. But they had a real social existence. No one in that long house ever went hungry unless the whole long house was hungry. There were no forsaken widows and orphans, no neglected old people. If the breadwinner was sick, there were others to do his work. The hygiene of the long house might not be all that present-day plumbing would demand but, as I often say, a long house depends on the angle at which you look at it. If it is horizontal, that is pagan and primitive and promiscuous, but if it is vertical, it is a city tenement. And I know slums in our advanced societies and I know that the hygiene, the morals and the neighborliness of the pagan long house is superior to those. What, I wondered, will science and technology do to that simple and decent (yes, decent) community? Give them duodenal ulcers in place of tropical ulcers and neuroses in place of yaws? Give them the jukebox in place of Jabu?

4. CRATED CIVILIZATION

This excursion into the jungles of Borneo is not a digression. Those of us who have grown up with science and technology cannot dissociate ourselves from it and stand back and look at it. Nor do we remind ourselves that this Technological Civilization is barely two hundred years old—barely as old as the United States of America. But there is another way to view it, and that is from the standpoint of other communities which have not grown up with it, but which are being suddenly confronted by it. None will be able to resist it, but they can either take it as a crated, prefabricated civilization, a sort of mail-order booking, or they can adapt and assimilate the essentials and use them to enhance the real values of their own way of life. It depends whether they want the jukebox or better seed; whether they want penicillin to cure their yaws and transform their lives or a chromium-plated bicycle to hang, fetish-wise, from the rafters.

And this is not irrelevant to ourselves. Science can give us things we need; or things we want; or things we do not know we want until it presents us with them; and also it can give us a thing we do not want but accept because "it is scientific." In place of

Ludditism and the smashing up of machines, there is a tendency to be too uncritical of scientific and technological benefactions. Science is A Good Thing, but it is not an end in itself; it is a means toward an end and that end is human betterment. As scientists keep insisting, there is neither good nor bad in any scientific discovery; it is the use to which it is put which makes it beneficial or dangerous; and the decision does not lie with the scientists themselves but with society, of which you and I are part, and of which they are functional citizens. It is right that we insist that with their knowledge of the potentials they should inform and guide us. We cannot evade our responsibility for the misuse of their discoveries, but neither can they. Public opinion cannot form judgments, and decide wisely if we do not understand the processes of science or the meaning of new developments.

5. THE RADIANCE OF A THOUSAND SUNS

IT IS REPORTED THAT J. ROBERT OPPENHEIMER at that instant when the first atomic bomb exploded in New Mexico had one thought in that blinding flash—a quotation from *Bhagavad-Gita,* The Hindu Song of God:

> If the radiance of a thousand suns were burst at once into the sky, that would be like the splendour of The Mighty One. . . .

and

> I am become Death, the shatterer of worlds.

At such a moment, the scientist could feel like Sri Krishna, master of Man's fate. But neither the man who directed the making of that bomb, nor those who decided to use it on Hiroshima and Nagasaki, can willingly assume "the Form of fire, world-wide, supreme, primeval." The burden of atomic destruction is too great for any man, or group of men—too great for the scientists, too great for the statesmen, too great for the generals. Here, indeed, is a godlike decision—the judgment as to whether the greatest scientific discovery ever made is to be used for human holocaust or human betterment.

Only an informed public opinion can determine that judgment

and only those who know the full implications—not the armchair strategists in the smoking room, but the scientists—can inform that public opinion. We have talked ourselves into a nightmare of fear, and a nightmare is the occasion for dreadful and irrational impulses and not for sensible judgments.

He would be a rash man who would say that the atom bomb, whether fission or fusion, will not be used, but we know that the Atom Powers are well aware that attack will beget reprisal and that that knowledge is an effective deterrent and may well be the final checkmate to war itself.

In the new situation, the United States offered the world a second chance—the first chance ended with the fiasco of the United Nations Atomic Energy Commission—in the form of President Eisenhower's proposal for an "Atom Pool" in December, 1953.

That proposal recognized that there were secondary "Atom Powers" which had neither bombs nor know-how, but which had indispensable atomic materials and wanted not atomic armories but atomic power plants. The source materials are abundant in regions which are themselves underdeveloped industrially—the Belgian Congo, South Africa, northern Canada, Australia, and (for thorium) India and Brazil—and which are not prepared to remain only the miners of atomic ores. These areas need energy for new industries; they need a short cut to industrial development. And that could lie in atomic power plants, which, as has already been discussed, have the great advantage of not requiring the constant fuel replenishment (and, therefore, an existing transport system) required by coal or oil plants.

Atomic energy might thus help to modify the great disparity between the so-called highly developed and the so-called underdeveloped territories. In that direction, and in the manifold uses of atomic by-products in medicine, in industry and agriculture, lies a positive and benign development of this great scientific advance.

6. "A BOLD NEW PROGRAM"

LESS ACUTE THAN THE FEAR OF THE MISUSE of atomic energy, but none the less real, is the world food problem. Of this there are no sirens to remind us and there are crammed silos and full larders to help those in the Western Hemisphere to forget. And the global figures are apparently reassuring—by 1954 the world food production figures were *per capita* balancing the population figures which, since 1939, had increased by two hundred million. Unfortunately, *per capita* and *per stomach* are not quite the same since most of the increased and, indeed, surplus production was in the Western Hemisphere, and in parts of Asia, the Middle East, Latin America and Africa the *per stomach* figure—the index of undernourishment —was worse than prewar. Meanwhile, Western farmers were anxiously concerned with their surpluses.

The situation recalled the doggerel epitaph of the victim of the agricultural slump of the 1930's:

Here lies the body of Farmer Pete
Who died of growing too much wheat.

To which was added the grim paradox:

And here's the Indian Achariya
Who died 'cos Pete's wheat wasn't here.

And it went on:

Statistics prove one must be shammin'
If there's too much food, there can't be famine.

But there can; there was; there is; and there will be until science and the wit and wisdom of Man can increase the *local* as well as the *global* food supplies. And that raises the challenge of the twentieth-century.

* * *

Professor Arnold Toynbee has suggested that in the broad sweep of history, this century will be chiefly remembered in future centuries, not as the age of political conflicts or technical invention (even of the atom bomb), but as the age in which human society dared to think of the welfare of the whole human race as a practical objective.

That was the vision of President Truman's "Point Four" in which he said:

"We must embark on a bold new program for making the benefits of our scientific advances and industrial progress available for the improvement and growth of underdeveloped territories."

It finds expression through the U. S. Mutual Aid projects, the British Commonwealth Colombo Plan and the operations of U. N. Technical Assistance. The aim is to help less privileged peoples to help themselves. If science ever had a positive social purpose and profound social implications, it is in this. And in ways which are more than just passing on the gadgets of a technological civilization. For while the emphasis is on economic improvement, the basis is "social engineering."

At base, there is the Gorgas Theme: *The Panama Canal could not be built until Surgeon-General Gorgas cleared the isthmus of yellow fever.* Similarly, the underdeveloped territories cannot be developed until they are rid of the mass diseases.

Resources of raw materials on which Western technology ultimately depends cannot be developed because the countries which possess them are undeveloped. Beneath a jungle may be fabulous resources but until that jungle, including the diseases which beset it, is cleared, they cannot be reached. And just as important as uncovering the resources in the earth is the importance of releasing the innate resources of the people themselves.

> The control of disease is a precondition of economic and social development. The advance of any community depends on the extent to which it reduces the burden of ill-health which squanders human resources, wastes food in nourishing bacteria and parasites, produces social lethargy and prevents peoples and countries from developing their full capacities. (Preliminary Report on the World Social Situation: United Nations Economic and Social Council.)

Through the advance of medical science, most of those diseases can now be cleared on a large scale. Millions have already had their lives touched and transformed. Hundreds of millions could be, likewise.

7. THE MISERY-GO-ROUND

DISEASE IS PART OF THAT MISERY-GO-ROUND of poverty: Disease—
Underproduction—Squalor—Ignorance—Malnutrition—More Disease. People who are sick cannot produce food nor earn money to
buy it. If they are ignorant as well as hungry, they cannot better
themselves. So they are malnourished, and malnutrition breeds
disease.

"But," say reasonable people, "if disease is prevented, all that
will happen will be that they will multiply and there will be less
food than ever. Better an infant should die than live to starve."

I once put this argument to a teen-age team on the radio. A
seventeen-year-old girl replied: "If I were told I could die pain-
lessly now or risk dying painfully in ten years time, I'd take the risk
—it might never happen!"

* * *

It need not happen, if agricultural scientists could move in
quickly behind the doctors, with better seeds; with better, but simple, methods of farming; with better, but again simple, equipment;
with the means to recover lost lands (like the kans-grass lands of
India, where a pernicious, tough-rooted weed-grass put millions of
acres out of cultivation), or malarial jungle, or thirstlands waiting
for irrigation; and with fertilizers, artificial and natural (like the
leguminous plants used as green manure for rice growing). With
them must go the experts on rural industries to draw overpopulation off the overcrowded acres and allow improved agriculture: and
teachers to tackle the ignorance which helps to keep people hungry
through lack of knowledge as to how they might improve their
crops and conditions.

All this is happening—I know because I have traveled the world
to see it—and it can be extended.

Fish is a quality food, and hundreds of millions are undernourished for lack of it. Yet fish could be farmed—not just hunted in
the seas. Inland fisheries can be developed and stocked. The Japanese, the Chinese and the Javanese know how to farm fish. In the
wet rice fields and terraces of Java, I have seen the fingerlings
"sown" when the fields were flooded for the rice growing and

"harvested" when the fields were drained. And there is the wonder-fish, the *Tilapia mossambica*.

This fish, indigenous to East Africa, is a mouth-breeder—it protects its spawn and its fingerlings in its mouth. How it arrived (by some piscatorial Kon-Tiki) in Southeast Asia is a mystery. In 1939, five specimens were found in a Javanese lagoon by a peasant. They were a heaven-sent blessing, for they multiplied prolifically. They were at home in salt water, in running water, in ponds or in the rice fields. And they were good to eat. Now they are being "broadcast" from Java, throughout Southeast Asia, into the Middle East and into the Caribbean Islands to provide desperately needed protein. In Thailand, honored visitors "plant" a hundred *Tilapia* as in the West V.I.P.'s plant a ceremonial tree.

In such ways, traditional ingenuity and twentieth-century science can combine to quiet the restless ghost of Malthus and answer those who would renounce humanity and deny the benefits of modern medical science to those who, "breeding like rabbits, should die like rabbits." If people are condemned to live like animals, they will breed like animals. And while, obviously, the population increase should be restricted, there should not be the threat "Unless."

8.   SCIENCE BELONGS TO HUMANITY

SCIENCE MAKES SENSE. It is the rational and reasonable approach to the problems of mankind as well as the creator of marvels and the revealer of wonders. The inquiring minds of the scientists will go on adventuring to the Endless Frontiers, beyond the horizons of common understanding. Let them; our covered wagons will follow presently where they have pioneered. They will persist in their sign language. Let them, provided they explain what we want to know. But do not let them mystify us; it is bad for them and worse for us.

This book started by trying to show that science belongs to the humanities. The concern of all of us should be to see that science belongs to Humanity!

Index